# JUSTICE
## FOR THE DEAD

### FORENSIC PATHOLOGY
### IN THE HOT ZONE

**Malcolm Dodd and
Beverly Knight**

Lothian
BOOKS

Thomas C. Lothian Pty Ltd
132 Albert Road, South Melbourne, Victoria 3205
www.lothian.com.au

First published 2006

National Library of Australia
Cataloguing-in-Publication data:

Dodd, Malcolm.
    Justice for the Dead: Forensic Pathology in the Hot Zone.

    ISBN 0 7344 0844 7.

    1. Forensic pathologists—Australia—Biography.
    2. Forensic pathology—East Timor.  3. Forensic pathology—
    Serbia—Kosovo.  4. Forensic pathology—Solomon Islands.
    I. Knight, Beverly.  II. Title.

614.1

Cover picture: Malcolm Dodd and Caroline de Koning just after the
post-mortem examination of an exhumed body at Sughu in the Solomon
Islands. September 2003.

Typeset in 11/15 pt Adobe Garamond
Cover and text design by Pages in Action, Melbourne
Typeset by Hedera, Melbourne
Printed in Australia by Griffin Press, Adelaide

# Dedication

*MD — To Caro and Mel*

*BK — To Maya, Alexander, Nicholas and Jesse*

# JUSTICE FOR THE DEAD

# Contents

# Acknowledgements

I am greatly indebted to all of the wonderful colleagues I have had the pleasure to work with over the years. The early missions to East Timor were largely experimental. I gratefully acknowledge the professional support and assistance given to me, particularly during mission one by Matthew Skinner, physical anthropologist, Shayne Towers-Hammond, an International Force for East Timor (INTERFET) soldier who was press-ganged into mortuary work and also the enormous support and encouragement provided by the remaining members of the INTERFET team, United Nations (UN) personnel, and civilian police. As the missions became more refined, we were fortunate to have the services of two dedicated women from the Argentine Forensic Anthropology Team (EAAF), Anahi Ginarte and Sofia Egana. Also, the assistance of Filomena Gomes, Laura Maia and Francelino Freitas was invaluable.

My time in Kosova in May of 2000 was greatly enhanced by the members of the British Forensic Team, working under the auspices of the UN and the UN International Criminal Tribunal for the Former Yugoslavia (ICTY). As a veteran of some twelve overseas missions to date, I regard the Kosova experience as the most sophisticated, given that we were allowed to use a dedicated mortuary facility and had, in contrast to other missions in other parts of the world, a complement of specialists including forensic anthropologists, scene-of-crime officers, photographers and a dedicated radiographer. The excellent staff and equipment enormously facilitated the rapid examination of a multitude of victims who died as a result of the civil war in the Balkans.

Mission one in Guadalcanal in the Solomon Islands, perhaps proved to be the most challenging of missions to date. The mission involved being dropped into the jungle by helicopter and performing three autopsies on a wooden plank at the gravesite in the most adverse of conditions. The camaraderie among the team members of the Regional Assistance Mission to Solomon Islands (RAMSI), produced nothing short of magical results. I am greatly in debt to my forensic technician for the first two missions to the Solomon Islands, Caroline de Koning. Caroline had no prior experience in third world forensic pathology, but proved herself to be exceedingly professional and an excellent travelling companion. To my detriment, I failed to keep a personal diary for these missions, and therefore I thank Caroline again for allowing me to use her diary as an aide memoire in the compilation of the first two chapters on the Solomon Islands. I would also like to acknowledge the great assistance and support given by Detective Sergeant John McIntyre of the Australian Federal Police (AFP)–RAMSI. At the time of the inception of this book, John displayed great encouragement and was responsible for reviewing the detail and accuracy of the early chapters on the Solomon Islands.

The last four missions to the Solomon Islands were largely based at the National Referral Hospital in Honiara, Guadalcanal, but on several occasions the team, including me, ventured into the dense jungles of the Weathercoast to perform the exhumations before transferring the bodies back to the capital. Dr Melanie Archer, Consultant Forensic Entomologist to the Victorian Institute of Forensic Medicine (VIFM), was my forensic technician on these missions. Although she is not specifically trained in this field, she excelled in the dreadful task of exhumation and examination of grossly decomposed bodies. Melanie was wonderful company during the many weeks spent in the Solomon Islands. I also acknowledge Melanie's valuable input and comments during the compilation of the Solomon Island chapters.

All chapters have been recorded onto a portable dictaphone and later transcribed and crafted by my co-author Beverly Knight. In all honesty, my part in this work was by far the easiest, as each hour of dictation translated into many hours of transcription grammar and syntax correction and modification to allow my work to be intelligible. At all times, Beverly has been a pillar of support, always contactable and generous with her time.

I would also like to thank Teresa Pitt, Senior Commissioning Editor at Lothian Books. Without Teresa's approach and encouragement, this book would not exist. The brief meeting Beverly and I had with Teresa and Peter Lothian, Managing Director of Lothian Books, was an exceedingly encouraging one and Beverly and I were both humbled to be asked to compose such a work. The time taken to compose these chapters has passed quickly in retrospect. The process of compilation, editing, cover design and supplementation of photographs has proceeded without incident, and for this we are both extremely grateful.

Lastly, but certainly not least, I would like to acknowledge the encouragement given to me by my wife Martine, and my wonderful children, Lisa and Andrew.

Malcolm Dodd
Melbourne, 2005

# Preface

This book has come about mainly due to the insistence of my friends and colleagues that this is a story that has to be told. Its evolution has not come easily.

Many months ago, a newspaper article outlining my forensic work in Solomon Islands was published, and in its closing paragraphs, a mention was made of a textbook that I had compiled on the study of terminal ballistics. At that time, the textbook was awaiting a publisher. As a result of this article, I was approached by Lothian Books to see whether I would be willing to compile my experiences in third world countries into a book for general readers. My initial reaction was to decline this offer. I had neither the time nor the inclination to put pen to paper.

By chance, however, my co-author Beverly Knight was hoping to compile a book on the function and special areas of the Victorian Institute of Forensic Medicine (VIFM). After attending a talk about my work in East Timor, Kosova and the Solomon Islands, Beverly approached me to see whether I would be interested in contributing to this project. While the project on the activities of the VIFM has not yet gone ahead, I mentioned to

Beverly that I had been approached by Lothian Books to write about my experiences, but that I had declined the offer. Beverly, to her credit, persuaded me that she would be very interested to assist in this project. The book that you have in front of you now is the result of this combined venture.

All the cases outlined in this work are factual. The research and experiences come largely from my personal diaries and those of my co-workers, contemporaneous post-mortem reports and literally thousands of slides taken in the field and at autopsy. The book outlines the highs and lows, the planning and the pitfalls and, ultimately, the immense satisfaction I gained from helping establish the cause of death and identity of victims in environments that challenge the normal work practices of a specialist forensic pathologist. The working environments span the entire spectrum of facilities, ranging from a sophisticated university department in Kosova to a rudimentary and makeshift post-mortem facility in Dili, East Timor, to the dense jungles of the Solomon Islands. Some fine detail has been left out, particularly in the chapters concerning the Solomon Islands, as many cases are before the law courts at the time of writing, and therefore are sub judice.

Thank you indeed for purchasing this book. I hope it brings both enjoyment and insight into the challenging world of forensic pathology as applied to third world countries and theatres of war. Finally, I hope that this book may encourage medical practitioners and specialist forensic pathologists to challenge themselves to undertake this most demanding of all tasks.

# ONE

# BACKGROUND

People often ask me what type of person you need to be to be a forensic pathologist. I tell them that I am no different to anyone else, I have the same emotions, but I have had to learn to be professionally detached from the circumstances of the person lying on the slab in front of me. Overall, my work is a scientific endeavour; I have to keep an emotional distance from it. Although I see people who have died under horrific circumstances, and while the fragility of life is graphically demonstrated to me more than it is to most other people, I don't particularly dwell on death or my own mortality. I love my work, and wouldn't want to do anything else. I enjoy the scientific challenge of putting together the pieces of the puzzle that will explain how someone met their death. I also feel that I am in some way making a positive contribution to society when I give evidence in court that will assist in the cause of justice.

As I say, I am just a normal bloke. I am fifty-two years old, and have been married for thirty years. I have two children: a daughter aged twenty-three and a son aged twenty-one. I was born in South

Australia in 1953 and moved to Victoria when I was six when my father moved for business reasons. I spent most of my childhood in North Balwyn. After I was married, we bought our first home in Boronia, and then moved to Bayswater where I set up my general practice. After eight years, we moved to a ten-acre hobby farm at Macclesfield near the Dandenongs and lived there for another eight years. I commuted to the city for one year when I became a forensic pathologist. We sold up about a year ago, and now live in Lysterfield, which is much closer to the city. I am a keen amateur astronomer, and I had a little observatory on the property at Macclesfield with a domed building. There, I had beautiful clear skies to look at, but I am now reduced to looking at murky suburban skies. I am a self-taught artist, and can knock up a reasonable landscape with oils. I'm also an avid collector of antique medical, surgical and scientific rarities.

My interest in chemistry began in my primary school years and evolved during high school and throughout my adult life to my current position as a forensic pathologist. My first laboratory was set up in my father's garage and expanded until it took over my whole bedroom. While I was still in primary school, one of my home experiments resulted in a near lethal explosion when a bottle exploded. It blew my clothing off, showered me in acid, gave me some nasty glass cuts on my leg and thumb and deafened me for a short time. Rather than put me off, this experience encouraged me to refine my techniques. I was a typical science geek at school, preferring to be in the science lab or library rather than outside kicking a football. My only sporting pursuit is pistol shooting.

## THE LONG ROAD TO FORENSIC PATHOLOGY

I am a product of the state school system. I went to Greythorn Primary School and Greythorn High School in North Balwyn. I left high school at the end of what is now known as year eleven. It was really a pragmatic decision to cut my losses. Although I was a devotee of physics, chemistry and biology, my mathematical skills were limited and I had a distinct lack of interest in history, English and foreign languages. This meant I was unlikely to achieve a brilliant year twelve, which might have led to university. In 1970, after finishing year eleven, I went to the then Royal Melbourne Institute of Technology (RMIT) to do the Associateship Diploma of Medical Laboratory Technology. I did this part-time, and qualified in 1976 with a major in haematology (study of blood). I also studied biochemistry (chemistry of the body), histology (anatomical microscopic structure of tissues), microbiology (micro-organisms) and cytology (cell biology).

While studying part time at RMIT, I worked full time at the Royal Australasian College of Surgeons in Spring Street, Melbourne, as a research assistant to Professor Douglas Coats. We pioneered total parenteral nutrition, which involves keeping a patient alive for the weeks after radical bowel surgery by intravenous feeding of a high caloric infusion and amino acid supplements. I stayed in that position for about a year and a half, and also became skilled in histological technique. I then moved on to work in the haematology and biochemistry labs at Chelmer Diagnostic Laboratories in St Kilda Road. After that, I worked at Box Hill and District Hospital in the biochemistry department for one year, and the histology department for a further two years.

The next step in my career was to become a laboratory technologist in a general practice in Ashwood. In this position, I performed all the rudimentary laboratory examinations pertaining to general practice, including basic biochemistry, haematology and microbiology. Although it was only my first year out after qualifying, I was paid as a lab manager, as I was responsible for running the laboratory and interviewing the representatives from supply companies. I also expanded the lab and set up many methodologies with higher quality control programs. I stayed there for about one and a half years. I was happy enough, but I had always had a burning desire to study medicine. Although my school results had made this impossible, I had done well as a trainee medical technologist. I had won the awards for Haematology I and Histology I, and was runner-up for Haematology II and Graduate of the Year. My wife, Martine, pipped me at the post in the latter two categories. I decided to try to get into medical school on the basis of my studies and experience to date rather than a year twelve qualification. I thought that Monash University was a more progressive institution than the University of Melbourne, and therefore more likely to accept my application. I applied to Monash, but I was told that I didn't have a chance of being accepted because I didn't have year twelve. They were not interested in my credits as a medical technologist, so that was the end of that.

I thought it couldn't hurt to try the University of Melbourne, so I approached them with pretty low expectations of success, and was surprised by their response. They weren't particularly concerned that I hadn't completed year twelve, and encouraged me to apply, telling me that I would be judged on my merits and experience. They warned me, though, that as I was a lateral entry candidate I would be required to enter second year medicine, not first year. There were only ten to twelve vacancies a year for lateral entry, including a number of people already in the system who were changing courses and who were therefore given preference. Keeping that in mind, I applied and wasn't altogether surprised when my application was rejected. The following year, I decided to apply again without telling my wife, as I assumed that I would be rejected again. I thought that if I got knocked back the second time, then at least I had given it my best shot, and I would have to resign myself to remaining a medical technologist. We returned from a holiday in Tasmania, and I picked out the envelope from the University of Melbourne from the pile of letters that had accumulated while we were away. I opened it and turned white as a sheet. Martine asked me what the matter was. I told her that I had applied to get into medicine at Melbourne University again without telling her and that I had been accepted. She asked me when I would start and, looking at the letter, I saw that it was the next day. So began my career in medicine.

The following day, I found myself in the dissecting room of the Anatomy Department with five other students. This was my first experience of full-time tertiary education and the study load was a shock to my system, as I was still working at the Ashwood laboratory. I felt that I couldn't leave them without warning or a replacement, so I continued as their medical technologist and some-how managed to fit in the full-time workload out of hours. Halfway through the year, they found a replacement for me at the lab, and so then I could concentrate on full-time study.

Although I didn't find the second year medicine subjects dif-ficult, I found the sheer magnitude of the workload in anatomy, physiology and biochemistry at second year level very demanding. While I was grateful that the University of Melbourne had offered me the opportunity to study medicine, they had told me quite openly that if I failed I would be out. Not only that, but that they would not allow any other lateral entry candidates from the medi-cal technology pool to follow me. As my medical career was on the line, as well as the opportunities of any who may want to follow me, it was a great relief that I passed. I then went onto third year medicine and then became a clinical medical student at St Vincent's Hospital in Fitzroy. I qualified in 1981.

I did a second stint at Box Hill Hospital, this time wearing a different hat. The first year was the compulsory internship year, which involved the usual rotation of medical, surgical, casualty and admitting officer. In my second year there, I was a junior resident medical officer, undertaking more rotations in casualty and paediatrics. I also covered the obstetrics, gynaecology and neonatal wards on a roster basis out of hours. That was a very demanding year, but it proved very fruitful, and it was at that time that I decided to set my sights on becoming a general practitioner. By this time Martine and I had one young child and another on the way, and the prospect of remaining in my current position for another five to six years didn't appeal greatly. It would involve very hard, prolonged study while living on a subsistence salary. I knew that it was time to head off in a new direction.

The following year, I leased a shop next to a chemist in a shopping complex and opened my general practice. I had done my market research and knew that the area needed a GP. Within a few months, I was seeing in excess of one hundred patients a week. By anyone's standards, seeing this number of patients after setting up general practice from scratch is exceptional. After a year or so, the workload was so demanding that I advertised for an associate. A colleague I had met in the hospital system joined me. After a year at that residence, we jointly bought a house several blocks up from the shopping centre, renovated it and turned it into a thriving general practice, which is still going strong today.

Although I enjoyed my work as a GP, after eight years I could see that the boom days of general practice were long over. I couldn't really see myself doing it for another twenty years without going nuts. One of the reasons for this was that with the advent of bulk billing, many patients would come to see me day after day with the most trivial of complaints. Even if just a few dollars separated them from a consultation, it would have dissuaded many of them from literally wasting my time. Also, under the bulk-billing system, doctors had to process patients rapidly, so those who had legitimate complaints would often not have enough time with the doctor. This system encouraged doctors to hand out prescriptions like jellybeans, as we just did not have the time to take a full history of the patient and perform a detailed examination. This essential skill is lacking in many new graduates who have to work under such conditions.

My satisfaction with general practice waned over time under these conditions, and the lure of pathology hadn't left me. Having obtained my basic medical degree, which is a prerequisite to do pathology, I applied to become a pathology registrar (trainee specialist) at Box Hill Hospital. I was accepted and sold my half of the general practice to my associate. This meant leaving my fairly affluent lifestyle as a GP behind to become an impoverished registrar. The drop in income meant that I had to sell my recently acquired 4WD because I couldn't afford to run it. We could no longer take overseas holidays and our social life was curtailed, but it was the area of medicine that really attracted me, and we decided that it was worth the sacrifice in income in the short term so I could pursue a more meaningful career.

I started at the hospital for the third time wearing yet another hat. I spent two years there and then moved on to Monash Medical Centre in Clayton for another two years. As I had always had an interest in forensic pathology, and now that I was well on the path to becoming a pathologist, I decided to concentrate on entering that field. It is hard for me to define the exact reasons for that now. I was an addict of the television show *Quincy M.E.*, probably the forerunner of all the crime scene investigation and forensic shows now. I think that's probably where my interest in the field of forensic medicine started. I thought it would be a fantastic job because I'd always had an interest in medicine and the sciences and forensic pathology combines all of that plus more.

The critical step on my path to becoming a forensic pathologist came when I successfully applied for the position of registrar at the Victorian Institute of Forensic Medicine (VIFM). I acted in the position of registrar for two years and qualified as a specialist forensic pathologist in 1997. In an unbelievable stroke of luck, one of the forensic pathologists resigned during my final year as registrar. Professor Stephen Cordner, the Director of the Institute, kept that job open for me so that when I got my ticket I stepped into the position of a consultant forensic pathologist. The VIFM is the only place in Victoria where you can do forensic pathology, and there are only six positions, which are filled by people who are there for the long haul. This was the job I had been working towards all these years, and I was very lucky to get it. I've been doing the job for eight years now (ten including my time as a registrar) and I have been very happy. I've had opportunities to undertake overseas work, which not everybody wants to do, but which I find very fulfilling and challenging both professionally and personally. I've been to East Timor five times, Kosova once and the Solomon Islands five times for forensic work and many other times to give expert evidence in court. I'm thriving on it; it is the best decision I've ever made. The role has changed my outlook on life. It may seem something of a paradox, but I was a fairly stressed GP. Now I am a relaxed forensic pathologist.

Before qualifying as a Fellow of the Royal College of Pathologists of Australasia in 1997, I graduated with an Associateship Diploma of Medical Laboratory Technology, and in between I was accepted as a Fellow of the Australasian College of Biomedical Sciences on the basis of submitted original research work. During my career as a forensic pathologist, I studied for the Diploma of Medical Jurisprudence from London. I got that in 2000. Another important aspect of my job involves education. I am responsible for coordinating the final year medical students from Monash University who come to the VIFM to get a two-day compressed course on the principles of forensic medicine and pathology. I deliver four to five lectures in that two-day period, and am also heavily involved in the teaching of our overseas graduates as well. To improve my teaching skills, I was part of the first intake of a new course, the Graduate Certificate of Health Professional Education, at Monash University. I got that qualification in 2003.

## CORONIAL SERVICES OF VICTORIA

Under the Coroner's Act (1985), the State Coroner's Office of Victoria gets involved in a death when a person dies unexpectedly, from accident or injury, or in a violent or unnatural way. It is involved when someone was 'held in care' as either a voluntary or involuntary psychiatric patient immediately before their death, or if a doctor has been unable to sign a death certificate giving the cause of death. The Coroner is also involved when the identity of the deceased person is unknown, when directed by the Attorney General and when the Coroner agrees to requests from members of the public to investigate particular cases. The Coronial Services of Victoria is located at Southbank in Melbourne, and is made up of the State Coroner's Office of Victoria and the VIFM. Both agencies work together to investigate violent or unnatural deaths with the aim of preventing such deaths.

The Coroner's role is to establish the identity of the deceased and the cause and circumstances of the death. The investigation by the various bodies attached to the Coroner's Office ends in the preparation of a 'brief' of evidence, which is a compilation of witness statements, expert reports, photographs and other documents and information from which the Coroner assesses how the situation will be handled. The VIFM provides a medical and scientific investigatory service for the Coroner.

Under the Act, the Coroner can make recommendations on public health and safety. Forensic pathologists regularly identify deaths that could have been prevented, such as those caused by industrial and other accidents, and those caused by genetic diseases or diseases resulting from exposure to certain substances. We inform the Coroner about these cases, and the Coroner may then issue a public safety warning or advise family members of the risks of injury or death. In a recent submission to the first parliamentary review of the Coroner's Act in twenty years, the State Coroner, Graeme Johnstone, is suggesting that the State Government tighten up the rules for doctors reporting deaths to the Coroner's Office. His proposals include more surveillance and oversight of death certificates and clearing up ambiguities in the definition of what constitutes an unnatural or unexpected death. The Coroner believes that there are many hospital and nursing home fatalities escaping scrutiny. The motto of the State Coroner's Office of Victoria is 'We Speak for the Dead to Protect the Living'.

## LIFE AS A FORENSIC PATHOLOGIST

Forensic pathology is the study of the human body to determine the cause and manner of death. People get these terms confused, though they are quite distinct. If you find that someone has died as the result of a shooting, the *cause* of death is a gunshot wound. You may judge the *manner* of death to be homicide, suicide, or accidental, depending on the circumstances.

The main difference between forensic pathology and hospital post-mortem work is that the chief area of interest in forensic pathology is the external rather than the internal examination. Where the cause of death is suspicious, or if death has been caused by trauma, the evidence is usually visible in the external examination and there is usually no underpinning disease contributing to the cause of death, or else it is incidental. Anatomical pathologists examine patients who have died as a result of disease and therefore they are more concerned with the internal examination of the deceased. Occasionally a forensic pathologist will come across significant natural disease, which has nothing to do with the death and is coincidental to the finding. This information can be of great importance to the family, though. While examining a victim who has died as result of a car accident, for example, we may find the presence of cancer, an inherited or congenital disease. When this happens, we first inform the donor tissue bank. Then the medical practitioners are told so they can counsel the family, in particular the first-degree relatives. Finding bowel cancer, for example, means that the first-degree relatives have an increased chance of later developing the same disease. They need to know so that they can take preventative measures.

'Forensic' means that the findings are presented in a court of law where necessary. Every suspicious case and homicide that we examine may result in a committal hearing and ultimately a trial. We are called in to testify as expert witnesses, in most cases at both the committal and the trial, unless the accused pleads guilty. This can mean between thirty and forty court appearances a year.

Judging by the number of books and television shows on forensic pathology, it has certainly captured the public imagination. But many people are scared off this area as a profession by the idea of having to give evidence in court many times a year and sometimes being questioned aggressively by experienced defence barristers. Perhaps as a result of this, there are very few forensic pathologists in Australia. Although there are about 1600 pathologists registered by the Royal College of Pathologists of Australasia, there are only about twenty-five full-time specifically trained forensic pathologists in the whole of the country. Forensic pathology clearly doesn't appeal to many pathologists. All trainee doctors are exposed to a limited number of autopsies, and quite frequently they just observe and don't perform them. When you are a pathology registrar, you are expected to perform about a hundred to a hundred and fifty autopsies, including at least ten forensic cases. Most anatomical pathologists don't particularly like performing autopsies, so once they have qualified, they delegate it to the registrars under the supervision of the consultants. As forensic pathologists, however, that is what we primarily do. As one of my interstate colleagues, Kevin Lee puts it, we are the blowflies of pathology.

Of the 3385 cases admitted to the VIFM in 2003–2004, fifty-eight per cent of the deaths were due to natural causes, thirteen per cent were the result of accident, thirteen per cent were the result of suicide, thirteen per cent were due to unknown causes, and three per cent were due to homicide. Some bodies are looked at only to inspect the death certificate, and some we come to a reasonable conclusion about without actually proceeding to a full autopsy because we have the medical history in hand. This probably accounts for about a thousand bodies, including some where the relatives object to the autopsy on religious or other grounds. Most of our work is fairly routine. I perform somewhere around three hundred routine autopsies a year. This translates into a lot of work: the autopsy itself, the examination of tissues under the microscope and writing up the report. In suspicious cases, specialist reports like toxicology and occasionally anthropology or entomology need to be added to produce a solid report that can be used in court for both prosecution and defence.

Although people assume I am constantly involved in dramatic murder investigations, examining homicide victims is only a small part of my work. As the yearly homicide rate in Victoria is currently around a hundred cases, each of the pathologists at the VIFM examine about twenty homicide cases each a year. Last year I examined twenty-four, which is the highest number I've done so far in any year. The bulk of my work is concerned with the examination of victims of sudden and unexpected natural death, such as heart attacks, strokes or epilepsy. Over fifty per cent of the total number of cases admitted last year were people aged over sixty years. It is also necessary to ascertain the cause of death in elderly people who have died without a death certificate being issued even where there are no suspicious circumstances. People aged over ninety have probably reached that age because they are quite healthy and haven't required any medication. They wouldn't have seen a doctor for quite some time, so no certificate would have been issued. Under the Coroner's Act, we are compelled to perform an examination in these cases.

Conducting routine autopsies includes being part of the homicide roster, which involves being on-call for one week in every four or five weeks. When I am on homicide roster, I am on-call twenty-four hours a day from Friday morning to the next Friday morning. During that time, sometimes nothing happens, sometimes everything happens. I have gone whole weeks where I've not been called once, and I've had times where I've had five or six homicide autopsies in one week. The most I have had to examine was six deaths in one week. That particular week consisted of the Wales-King murders, an axe murder, a skeleton to examine, and two highly suspicious cases.

Causes of death in homicide include blunt force trauma, multiple stabbings, shootings, quite a few cases of strangulation and one or two of deliberate poisoning. The cause of death in most murder cases involves blunt trauma, stabbing, manual strangulation and lastly, gunshot injury. This is in contrast to the US, where most homicides are the result of shooting. Probably only about ten or fifteen per cent of homicides in Victoria are the result of gunshot injury. Sometimes cases that have been flagged as suspicious have turned out not to be. Alternatively, sometimes a case that is flagged as routine has turned out to be homicide. An example of this was an examination of an old man I conducted years ago. I attended the scene of the death and the man looked like an alcoholic who had probably died of natural causes. I could only see a few minor cuts and scratches on his body and neither I nor the investigating officers considered his death to be suspicious. But during the autopsy, when I did the neck dissection, I found multiple bruises around the neck, clearly indicating manual strangulation. This remains an unsolved homicide to this day.

Apart from homicide and sudden and unexpected death from natural causes, the deaths that are investigated by the Coroner include suicides, deaths caused by road accidents (pedestrians, drivers, passengers), industrial deaths, deaths in the home, deaths caused by fire, drowning, drug overdose and sudden infant death syndrome (SIDS), anaesthetic deaths, deaths in surgery where there may have been a surgical mishap, deaths related to adverse drug reaction and deaths in custody. The number of deaths caused by accident and suicide are fairly similar, sad to say. The most common methods of suicide include drug overdose, hanging and carbon monoxide poisoning (inhalation of car exhaust fumes). Less common methods include jumping from a building or the Westgate Bridge. Even less common is suicide by shooting and occasionally by drowning or jumping in front of a train.

Sometimes, we aren't able to identify a cause of death, even after a full autopsy and all sorts of other ancillary tests. These deaths are mostly young, otherwise healthy adults, and occasionally older children. We may presume a cardiac irregularity, although in many cases it is beyond proof.

In a typical week of fifteen autopsies chosen at random from my log book, two related to heart disease, one was suicide by intentional overdose, one was a gunshot suicide, one was a heroin overdose, two were deaths by fire, one was due to stroke, one was due to a blood clot to the lung from deep vein thrombosis, two were due to child abuse, one was alcohol-related, one was from acute blood loss, one was accidental crushing by a tractor and one was an intra-operative death. A typical day at work involves two or three autopsies in the morning, usually from about ten o'clock to one o'clock. In the afternoon, I correct the first drafts of the reports of the cases I have performed and resubmit them to the stenographer. I then spend an hour or perhaps more at the microscope examining tissue slides from previous cases. Then I complete and check reports for the Coroner, which may include integrating specialist reports like toxicology, anthropology or radiology to produce the final report. We have meetings twice a week, where pathologists get together to discuss and demonstrate difficult and problematic cases. At certain times of the year, I also have teaching commitments such as lectures and tutorials. This routine work is punctuated by occasional visits to court in all of the different court systems and by the rostered week spent on-call for homicide cases.

Forensic pathology is inextricably concerned with tragedy. The accidents, the unnatural deaths and the sudden and unexpected deaths in otherwise healthy people are always tragic. It is particularly distressing to examine babies who have died of SIDS and toddlers who have drowned or have been run over by cars. In my profession, we see the very worst that people can do to one another. We see an extraordinary spectrum of trauma, violence and premeditated injuries. It isn't always easy, when performing an autopsy on a crime gang member, for example, to feel sympathy for that person. But someone will be mourning them: parents, a spouse, children. In my overseas work on war crime victims, I see the results of atrocities perpetrated by despots and militia leaders that just defy all reason. The human drama unfolding before me in my work never escapes me.

But professional detachment is essential. I have to separate myself from the emotional dimension of the circumstances so that I can efficiently do my job, which includes producing an unbiased report. Even if the case is a horrendous example of homicide, I must write an impartial report that simply states the facts. Contrary to common belief, forensic pathologists don't work for the prosecution. Even though most of our reports are used by the Department of Public Prosecutions, we are neutral witnesses and we are asked questions in court by both the defence and the prosecution.

I am in court for a lot of my professional life. While I was nervous when I was new to the job, I don't stress over any cases these days because I am confident about what I am dealing with and talking about. I have learnt not to show any feelings I might have about how a homicide was committed, for example, because I could compromise the case. So I separate myself from the tragedy I am involved in. At the same time, I get extremely frustrated when it is clear to me that someone is a victim of homicide and the perpetrator is given a light sentence, or is released or found not guilty. But I simply have to accept this. My personal views on a defendant's guilt or innocence are not relevant.

This type of work is not for everybody. Professional detachment is essential. I cannot allow myself the luxury of thinking too deeply about a case at an emotional level or I would be consumed by it and unable to function as a pathologist. It certainly is an unusual profession to be in, but I find it personally stimulating. It has provided me with enormous opportunities, and I enjoy the integration of the legal aspect with the principles of medicine, surgery, paediatrics, obstetrics, gynaecology, pharmacology and all of the other specialty areas, as well as the basic sciences of chemistry and biology.

## THE VICTORIAN INSTITUTE OF FORENSIC MEDICINE (VIFM)

The staff at the Victorian Institute of Forensic Medicine is headed by the Director, Professor Stephen Cordner and the Assistant Director, Associate Professor David Ranson. Dr Matthew Lynch is the Head of the Division of Forensic Pathology. The pathologists are Dr Michael Burke, Dr Noel Woodford, Dr Shelley Robertson and me. From time to time, we have full-time trainee registrars and, more often than not, a few Sri Lankan pathologists who come to us for further education and experience. We also have a very good photographic section, an information technology facility, stenographic staff and a comprehensive forensic library with a fantastic librarian, Kerry Johannes. Our mortuary technicians are all experienced staff. Some have come across from the old facility of the Flinders Street extension. The younger group are predominantly science graduates or specifically trained in the field. We have a dedicated team of experienced, focused professionals.

We have onsite specialist departments. The Histology Department prepares tissue slides for examination under microscope so we can find out the nature and extent of any natural disease or injury present that may be related to the cause of death. The Toxicology

Department is responsible for detecting drugs and poisons in biological tissues for medico-legal purposes. This involves analysing blood and other specimens for alcohol, drugs of abuse and pharmaceutical drugs. The Molecular Biology Department provides DNA typing services for the identification of human remains and paternity suits. The Anthropology Department determines the origin and identity of skeletal remains, such as gender, race, stature and age of the deceased. The Odontology Department compares dental records to identify the remains of people who are unable to be visually identified for a variety of reasons, including the effects of fire or putrefaction. Dr Melanie Archer heads the Entomology Department. Forensic entomology uses insect activity on bodies as a timeline for estimating the minimum time since death. This is especially useful when the time of death is an important factor or is in dispute.

The facilities at the VIFM are state of the art—it is arguably one of the best facilities worldwide. The building is relatively modern and the mortuary facility is excellent. It is perhaps a little different to other mortuary facilities. It is a large common workplace with a blue painted concrete floor, stainless steel benches and overhead surgical lighting. There are onsite x-ray facilities and a recently acquired CT scanner. Most pictures of mortuaries show fixed porcelain or stainless steel tables on pedestals. Our set-up is different. We have mobile stainless steel trolleys, so that the body stays on the trolley from admission to discharge. During the autopsy it is locked into the workbench and becomes part of the infrastructure. This is a very sensible arrangement, as it means the bodies don't have to lifted. On any given morning, particularly on a Monday, which tends to be the busiest day after the weekend casualties, there can be four or five pathologists all working in the mortuary. Each pathologist would do two or three cases a morning, giving a total of about ten to twelve autopsies a day.

## HOMICIDE

Forensic pathologists are on-call for homicide duty one week in every four or five weeks. During that week, the pathologist needs to be contactable at all times. I used to have a pager, but now have a mobile phone. My plans have to be very flexible for that week. I have learnt not to go out to the cinema or to a good restaurant to sit down and relax for a few hours. There is nothing worse than going out to a sophisticated restaurant only to be called away before I've had a chance to order, or even worse, after I've ordered but before I've eaten. Although I may not be called out at all in that week, I need to behave as if I will be at any moment. Obviously, I can't have more than an occasional drink, and it is difficult to fall into a deep sleep. When I'm on call, if the phone rings while I am asleep, it just has to ring once and I'll have it in my hand and be able to make perfect sense, which says something about my level of sleep. When I am not on-call, I can sleep through the phone ringing.

While on-call, anything can happen at any time. I can be called out during work hours to attend a crime scene, or late at night or early in the morning. As we are responsible for the forensic examination of homicides committed anywhere in Victoria, I sometimes travel very long distances. Over the years, I have probably been to most parts of Victoria to be part of the investigation team in the cases of suspicious deaths and homicides. We are only given helicopter or light aircraft transport in exceptional circumstances, so we need to be rested and alert enough to drive to the crime scene—even when it's hours away. There have been times when I have worked the whole day, gone home, had tea, and then been called out to somewhere three hours' drive away. After examining the crime scene, I've had to drive back again. Then I've had to perform the autopsy as soon as the body was delivered to the Institute—sometimes immediately, sometimes early the next morning.

## THE CRIME SCENE

While it isn't considered necessary for the forensic pathologist to attend the scene of the crime for all homicides, I believe it is very important to do so. I invariably gain something from every scene examination, even in an obvious homicide, like a victim who has received several bullets to the head. During the autopsy, I may find small injuries that seem nondescript, but that are hard to understand in the autopsy room and that the photographs don't explain. But if I have seen the body in location, I may be able to rationalise the nature of the injury because I know, for instance, that there was furniture that the victim may have fallen against or been hit by. By examining the scene, I can gain further insight into the injuries, making it easier to interpret them. So I attend the crime scene even if I am told that it is a straightforward case and I don't need to be there.

I have learnt, though, that if the crime scene is somewhere as far afield as Bendigo, it's a good idea to find out how things are progressing at the scene before I leave home. It is a mistake to arrive too early. If I arrive before the body has been photographed and the video of the scene and the body in location has been taken, I may have to wait around for several hours before I can examine the body. I have also learnt that it is worth asking for more photographs to be taken than the normal range. These extra photographs can be useful in developing scenarios to help interpret injuries; they are also invaluable material for teaching.

There was a case in the country several years ago where a man was found lying dead and naked in his house. He had fallen through a glass door in his house, had cuts and lacerations all over him, and there was blood everywhere. It looked like a suspicious case, as the coffee table and other furniture had been upturned. It really looked like a nasty crime scene. The police thought this could possibly be a homicide as the result of an aggravated burglary. It turned out to be a classic case of hypothermia. When someone is dying of hypothermia, or extreme cold, they can paradoxically feel hot and take their clothes off—the 'paradoxical undressing', 'hide and die' syndrome. When this happens, the victims often stumble about and injure themselves. The man had died of exposure to cold, and, despite appearances, hadn't been robbed or bashed at all. I was able to form this opinion because I attended the scene and saw the state of the house, the broken glass from the door near the body and felt the freezing temperature. When we did the autopsy, I found the classic internal signs of hypothermia.

## AUTOPSY

The autopsy is pivotal in a homicide or a suspected homicide investigation. We attempt to identify the immediate cause of death, or at least the contributing factors leading to the death. In cases of suspicious death and obvious homicide, a major purpose of the autopsy is to discover and retrieve trace evidence such as nail scrapings from under the fingernails. We can also look for foreign DNA, evidence of sexual abuse, rape, evidence of child abuse and bruising. We may x-ray bodies in an attempt to identify old fractures, or where the body is in an advanced state of decomposition. We may take fingerprints either before, during, or sometimes after the autopsy. In cases of shooting, we call upon one of the ballistics experts from Victoria Forensic Science Centre at Macleod to take notes of the bullet injuries while we are performing the autopsy. If possible, we extract the bullet from the body and hand it over to the ballistics experts, so that they can try to match the bullet with the gun. All the items of evidence—hair, tissue, fluids for toxicology, items of clothing, nail scrapings, swabs in cases of sexual assault, projectiles—are all packaged up in a 'chain of custody' mode. This means that everything is signed for and handed over to the appropriate officials so that we are able to trace who has handled each exhibit. Also, in homicides and suspicious deaths, or in cases of special interest like aviation deaths or diving fatalities, detailed internal and external photographs are taken.

Performing a routine autopsy is done with the help of a mortuary technician. Most of us gravitate towards a technician we work well with. The exception is when we are on-call; then we work with whoever is rostered at the same time. The usual protocol for autopsy begins with the forensic technician undressing and videotaping the body on admission to the mortuary refrigerator. The pathologist then examines the body in a very detailed fashion, dictating the findings into a dictaphone. Once all the details of the external examination are noted, we begin the internal examination. In suspicious cases, we generally remove the brain first, though in routine cases this is often done last. We reflect the scalp by an incision from ear to ear over the top section. We pull the frontal scalp forward and the back of the scalp backwards to expose the cranium. We use a skull saw or a bone saw to cut around the skull so the brain can be removed and examined. This also allows the veins of the neck to decompress to avoid haemorrhage into the neck muscles, which can sometimes mimic strangulation. Once that is done, the technician opens the body in a traditional Y-cut incision. This is a cut along each collarbone and then down the middle from the breastbone to the pubic bone. We then flay the skin from the rib cage, set it to one side, cut through the ribs with a pair of rib shears and remove the rib cage. Then we remove the organ block, from the level of the tongue down to the lower part of the large bowel. In most cases, the technician separates the small and large bowel from the remainder of the organs and puts it to one side.

After the technician has placed the organ block on an examination bench, the pathologist then meticulously dissects each organ in turn, weighing each one, commenting on normality or abnormality and taking relevant sections of tissue for histological analysis. The number of specimens we take for histology is fairly routine, but we take a great many more in cases like sudden infant death syndrome. Sometimes we take further specimens for analysis by toxicologists or for other analysis. While this isn't necessary where the case is an obvious stroke or heart attack, it may be necessary if a death is largely unascertained, or relates directly to alcohol or drugs, prescription or otherwise. Once we have examined the organs and have taken relevant samples, we put all the organs, including the brain, into a plastic bag and into the now combined cavity of chest and abdomen. We return the rib cage to its normal position and the technician reconstructs the body and washes and dries it in readiness for discharge to the relatives.

If the body is skeletal, or there are only some bones, such as the skull or the femur, we do the initial examination and then we refer it to the physical anthropologist. If the identity of the body is in question, we may call in the forensic odontologists, or we may take bone marrow and blood for DNA analysis by the molecular biologists. Where there are lots of maggots or flies on a decomposed body, and if the time of death is pivotal to the case, we enlist the help of the forensic entomologist. The majority of cases don't fall into these categories, however. It is only the occasional, suspicious case that demands anything more complex than a routine autopsy.

In a straightforward case, the whole process takes only about an hour or so, or even less in a case like someone dropping dead of a heart attack. The cases range from quick and routine to quite protracted and exceedingly complicated.

AREAS OF EXPERTISE

The variations in the cases we examine are enormous and we modify the autopsy technique if we need to. Some deaths require methods that are not part of a routine post-mortem. This is the case with scuba diver fatalities in particular, where we need to demonstrate the presence of gas bubbles in the circulation. This means cross-clamping the arteries at the base of the brain to trap any air bubbles that may have formed during a rapid, uncontrolled ascent and decompression. We also need to cross-clamp the veins and arteries leading into the heart to demonstrate gas in the cardiac chambers which would have occurred during decompression. This is quite a specialised procedure, and requires some expertise and experience to perform. I have become the de facto expert on such cases at the VIFM because I have done virtually all of them in the last ten years.

I have also gained expertise in gunshot wounds, having always had an interest in handling rifles, shotguns and pistols. In my younger days, I used to shoot rifles at Williamstown Rifle Range, which no longer exists, and now I shoot at a local pistol club. I coupled my personal interest in shooting with my professional experience of gunshot wounds as a forensic pathologist and compiled a definitive textbook on the subject. *Terminal Ballistics: An Atlas and Text of Gunshot Wounds* was recently published by CRC in Florida USA. It is my hope that the book will be useful to many people, including forensic pathologists and trainees, firearms examiners, and scene-of-crime officers as well as members of the legal profession. Having an area of special interest means I have been deemed to be an expert in that area. As well as providing ballistics opinions on Victorian cases, I have also been asked for independent opinions on interstate cases.

## HOMICIDE AUTOPSIES

The autopsy process becomes more complicated when there is a suspicious death and in cases of obvious homicide. The forensic pathologist carries out the whole process in the homicide room watched by the homicide squad and others. We x-ray all victims of homicide and suspicious cases and many burnt cases just to check for bullets that we may not otherwise see because the body has degraded. We leave the clothing on the body and examine each item carefully for evidence of injury, such as bullets, stabbing or bashing. We then remove the clothing one item at a time and photograph them in great detail. Once we have photographed and described the external injuries of the stripped body, we proceed with the autopsy.

In cases of homicide and suspicious death, the forensic pathologist performs a subcutaneous dissection. We flay to one side the skin of the backs of the fingers and the arms and sides, usually from the shoulder down to the wrist, to expose any areas of bruising that we might not have seen during the initial external examination and that may reveal evidence of a struggle or defensive injuries. Completing a detailed homicide investigation can take up to four to five hours. It is very important to get it right the first time, so we have to be meticulous in both the internal and external examinations. Once we have performed the autopsy, it is difficult to revisit the case and it is poor practice to miss obvious things. On rare occasions, a body is brought back from the undertakers for the pathologist to examine something further that may have come to light from the homicide squad or an informant after the fact, such as bruises or injuries that may not have been exposed during a routine examination.

All the evidence gathered during the autopsy process goes to construct a report, which often runs to fifteen pages or more. The report includes details of the internal and external examination, the results of the examination of tissue under the microscope (histology), and the integration of specialist reports where required, such as toxicology, molecular biology (DNA), anthropology and entomology. Once all the information is in, the pathologist compiles the report and is then able to draw a conclusion and make final comments about the cause and manner of death, contributing factors and significant incidental findings. The whole report is then used by one of two agencies, the Coroner or the homicide squad. The vast majority are routine Coroner's cases. They go to the Coroner for examination and end up either as an 'in-chambers finding', where the Coroner makes a decision on the basis of the evidence included in the file and comes to a finding (for example in a clear case of suicide), or as an open inquest. In an open inquest, members of the family, hospital staff and others who are involved in the case are called as witnesses. The finding is determined in that forum. In cases of murder or suspected murder, the report is passed on to the homicide squad. These cases traditionally go to committal in the Magistrates' Court where the body was found to see if there is evidence to proceed to trial. If it does proceed to trial and it is a homicide, the cases will probably be heard in the Supreme Court in William Street, Melbourne, irrespective of where the case was originally heard.

## EXPERT WITNESS

When I am required as an expert witness, I am served a subpoena. This happens weeks or months before the committal or trial, so I have enough time to retrieve and review the post-mortem report, the circumstances report, witness statements and the crime scene and autopsy photographs. I do this about a week before the case, then the night before and then the morning before the case. By the time I get into court and have been sworn in, I am confident that I know as much about that case as I can. If it is a contentious case, I may speak to the defence and prosecution to identify what the key issues of the case are. Sometimes I do some peripheral reading to bring myself up to date on new developments, procedures and treatment modalities that I may be asked about. It is essential to go into court fully prepared and it would be poor practice to do otherwise, as that could cause the case to fall apart. It is also absolutely vital for me to stick to my own area of expertise, because if I were to attempt to give an opinion on an area I was not qualified in, I could be successfully challenged on my knowledge and experience and again compromise the case.

Like the autopsy process, the trial process can be swift and uncomplicated, or it can be protracted and laborious. This depends on the complexity of the case and also on the tactics of the defence barristers. A regular tactic of defence barristers is to offer alternative scenarios to explain the pattern of injury on the victim in the case. When this happens, I can either say no, that the suggested alternative scenario is not consistent with the injuries, or yes, that it is consistent with the injuries. Even though I may think the alternative scenario unlikely and believe that the accused is guilty, if the scenario is a possible explanation of the injuries, I must say so. The forensic pathologist's evidence has to be completely neutral and unbiased. In these cases, however, I can add that I think one scenario is more likely than another.

I haven't had any experiences where there has been a dramatic showdown in court over my evidence. Unlike television dramas, the whole process is usually rather matter of fact. Occasionally cross-examination can get rather heated, and the defence may pester me about an alternative scenario that I don't entertain as a possibility. They may press me to say that it is possible and even though I may respond by saying that it is only remotely possible, they may just keep on pressing the point until they feel they have created some doubt about my evidence. I have to stick to my opinion, despite the verbal battering I may receive as a result. I was involved in a case once where a baby had allegedly been abused by the mother's de facto husband. The accused maintained that the child had received the injuries by rolling off the sofa. The examination of the child revealed a horrendous skull fracture. Given the distance of the drop, even onto bare floorboards, it was my opinion that this account of how the injuries was received was just not possible. I gave evidence that the fracture could not have occurred in any other way than through physical abuse, or a fall from a greater height, which wasn't a possibility in this case. I was questioned aggressively about this, but I refused to budge. The accused in this case eventually confessed.

Barristers range from quietly spoken individuals to those who border on the bombastic and theatrical. There are a few barristers around town who are known for theatrical behaviour and for badgering witnesses unfairly. If there is a jury present for a trial, they are generally not impressed by this sort of behaviour. I once had a barrister directly ask me from way out of left field whether I was biased. He put it to me that I was working for the police and he proposed that I had produced a biased report to suit the police's opinion on the case. His tactic was to try to discredit me right from the very beginning. This particular barrister is famous for going for the jugular and for trying to attack the man rather than the report. I took great pains to explain that I had not produced a biased report and that I was an impartial expert. His tactic didn't work.

Due to the confrontational and adversarial nature of the legal system, I need to be confident in my opinion and ready to fight to maintain it.

Conflicting opinions between expert witnesses happen all the time. It is common for me to be the expert acting on behalf of the prosecution and for the defence team to find another expert in a similar field with an opinion entirely contrary to mine. In a case I was involved in some years ago, a woman was misprescribed a cytotoxic drug (having a toxic effect on cells) for arthritis and developed total bone marrow failure. The defence in the inquest brought a fairly impressive clinician to give evidence. He tried to offer other explanations as to why this woman's bone marrow had crashed and suggested that she had died of infection. Once again, I gave my opinion that the only possible explanation in this case was a massive overdose of the drug. The defence tried to belittle my qualifications compared to the other expert's qualifications, but this didn't get them very far. Ultimately, the person left standing is the one who is controlled, dignified and authoritative without being boisterous or arrogant.

Surprisingly, in the five or six years it takes to become a qualified forensic pathologist, there is no component of the program dedicated to training to become an effective and confident expert witness in court. That is something that is slowly gained with experience. On my very first court appearance, which was for a homicide, I was shaking with fear in anticipation of the ordeal. In retrospect, I realised I could have done a lot better. I followed my more experienced senior colleagues to court on many occasions to watch them give evidence in committals, trials and inquests. Once I learnt the rules—to tell the simple truth and not to expand on areas beyond my level of expertise, not to fill in gaps and guess and not to say too much—the process became quite straightforward.

Following these rules, I have more or less kept out of trouble for the last eight years as a consultant. Also, by compiling a very detailed report, I find that I'm called very infrequently to the Coroner's Court for inquests, as virtually all of the questions they wish to ask have been addressed in the report.

Another aspect of the job involves being in the media spotlight. At crime scenes, there are invariably cameras. They can be close by and obvious, but they can also be half a kilometre down the road with a massive telephoto lens. I have seen myself on the news several times at various scenes examining a body or waiting to examine a body where I was not aware that any cameras were present. It is important to be sombre at crime scenes. If you get caught on camera smiling going to or from a crime scene, it doesn't look good. That was the very first thing Professor Cordner told me—do not smile at a crime scene!

## CASES OF INTEREST

During the course of my career, I have worked on many cases in which people have died tragically and violently. Some of these have been high profile cases. One of the most tragic cases I have worked on was the recent murder of little Gracie Sharpe. I examined Gracie's body and a colleague of mine, Noel Woodford, examined the remains of her mother, Anna Kemp. John Sharpe has recently been convicted of killing his wife and twenty-month-old daughter Gracie by shooting them in the head with a spear gun, dismembering his wife and dumping the bodies in a waste site at Mornington. He is currently serving two life sentences.

Another high profile case I worked on was the Wales-King double murder. A book was published on this case and I appear in chapter fourteen, which includes the description of the autopsies.

I've also had more than my share of gangland murders. I've performed autopsies on alleged Walsh Street police killer Victor Pierce, who was shot dead in an execution style drive-by shooting, Dino Dibra, who was gunned down outside his home, and Andrew 'Benji' Veniamin, who was shot dead at a Carlton restaurant. I also examined Jason Moran and Pasquale Barbaro, who were shot inside a van in a car park while they were watching a junior football clinic. They were killed in front of five children including Moran's six-year-old twins. Another high profile case I have examined was that of the slain mother Anita Pochopien, the victim of a driveway shooting.

A bizarre case I worked on involved the contract homicide of the husband of the female wrestler Donna Parsons, whose wrestling name was 'The Welsh Dragon'. She apparently wanted her husband's insurance money, so she enlisted the aid of a friend to kill him, claiming that he was an abusive husband. The hired hit man failed twice in his mission, so another willing perpetrator was found. The two men together managed to kill Paul Parsons on the third attempt on his life, by bashing him with a crowbar and slitting his throat. All three were convicted and sentenced to lengthy prison sentences. I have also dealt with several deaths in custody, and at least one police shooting.

One of the strangest cases I have ever been involved in has become known as the 'Sorrento Skeleton Case'. In 2001, a skull and some bones were found on top of a hill above Sorrento cemetery. I was called to the scene to examine the bones and I confirmed that they were human. At first, it looked as though the body had been buried and foul play was suspected. But it soon became clear that the body had simply become covered by sand in a naturally occurring process over the course of time. The following day, we went back to excavate the site and I exhumed pretty much an entire skeleton. Upon examining the bones more closely, I could tell that it was a female skeleton. It is possible to calculate the maturity of an individual by the level of fusion between certain bones in the body. As all the bone epiphyses were closed, I was also able to inform the police that the body was that of a mature adult beyond the age of twenty-six years. The length of the femur indicated that she would have been a rather tall woman. There was a set of full natural teeth present in the skull.

Then the case took an interesting turn. When I was removing the ribs of the skeleton from the remnants of clothing, an old-fashioned false breast was revealed. In addition to the information that the deceased was a fully mature female of tall stature, I could add that she had had a right mastectomy. This information greatly increased the chances of finding someone on the missing persons file. A little later, I was astonished to find a glass eye. The eye had a brown iris and I judged that it was probably from the right side. Feeling like a character from a crime scene investigation show, I rang the police again and told them that we now had further very specific evidence, which should help to narrow the search enormously.

A short time later, I found an old fashioned purse, which contained the remnants of pounds, shillings and pence. As decimal currency came in on 14 February 1966, I was able to ascertain that this was a pre-1966 death on the basis of this evidence alone. Due to the amount of time that had passed since the death, the police had to trawl through masses of paper files looking for a missing person who matched the description I had given them. Despite the cumbersome method of searching, the police were successful in finding the identity of the missing female within a matter of hours.

Once the identity of the deceased woman was established, we unravelled the whole tragic story. The missing woman was last seen going into a pharmacy in Sorrento and getting a full prescription of barbiturate medication. We had also found some old drinking bottles and a little cup and two old-fashioned brown pill bottles. There were no pills left in them, but examination of the residue inside the bottles revealed traces of barbiturates. This woman had terminal breast cancer, hence the removal of the right breast. Her illness may or may not have related to the glass eye. That remains the one part of the puzzle that I still don't understand. This poor woman had previously contemplated suicide by throwing herself under a train, but hadn't gone through with it at the last moment. She had then got a prescription for the barbiturates and, as far as her family and friends knew, she had disappeared off the face of the earth. She must have chosen this secluded spot, taken all of the tablets and died shortly after. It was incredible that in the intervening thirty-odd years her body had slowly been covered over with sand and had never been found.

The Coroner accepted her identity and her cause of death as barbiturate toxicity in someone who had terminal breast cancer. It turned out to be a truly astonishing case from a multidisciplinary point of view. Not only the pathology, but the exhumation, the examination of the bones, the trace evidence surrounding the site and the toxicology all came together to produce a definitive result at the very end. A positive outcome to this sad case was that the woman's children, who were now adults and had moved to Queensland since their mother's disappearance, were finally given the news that the body of their mother had been found. All they had known for over thirty years was that their mother had left home one day and never come back. They were able to give her a final burial ceremony and hopefully have some closure to their grief. That is one aspect of the job that I find rewarding; to be able to return the remains to loved ones, having confirmed the identity and reconstructed the circumstances of how they met their death. In this case particularly, it was very satisfying. This is the only case I have ever been involved in where the finding of the evidence and the fitting together of the pieces of the puzzle resembled any of the crime scene investigation shows on television. I often use this example when teaching—more as an example of how things usually do not work!

## INVESTIGATING WAR CRIMES

In my eight years as a consultant, and two years as a registrar, I have probably performed around four thousand autopsies. I have examined approximately twenty homicide victims a year at the VIFM, a total of about a hundred and forty or so, and have attended the court cases for most of them. In addition, I have also performed one hundred or more homicide autopsies in East Timor, around sixty in Kosova and about fifty in the Solomon Islands. More recently, I was involved in the international effort in Thailand after the tsunami in December 2004 destroyed the lives and homes of thousands of people in Asia. Unlike my work in East Timor, Kosova and the Solomon Islands, the tsunami cases were not crime-scene examinations, they were scenarios of mass disaster on a scale that none of us had previously encountered. This was quite a different experience and one that my colleagues and I still have trouble talking about, as we were so overwhelmed by the sight of so many dead bodies.

When I undertook my first overseas mission in 2000, however, nothing I had done in my work at the VIFM had prepared me for my overseas work with victims of war crimes. I had never investigated the victims of large-scale disasters of any kind. Unlike our excellent post-mortem facilities at the VIFM, the overseas work was done in environments where the facilities and equipment provided were extremely primitive. Also, the pattern of injuries resulting from the conflicts were quite different to those I come across in my day-to-day work in Melbourne. They were characteristically quite furious, involving frenzied hatcheting with machetes, heads and chests crushed with rocks and multiple gunshots from high velocity weapons and military firearms. I had, however, performed many autopsies at the VIFM on fresh cases, decomposed cases, horrendously decomposed cases and skeletons. I figured that I had developed a body of knowledge and expertise which in theory should be applicable in any given situation. This was my thinking when I volunteered to work on my first overseas mission in East Timor in January 2000.

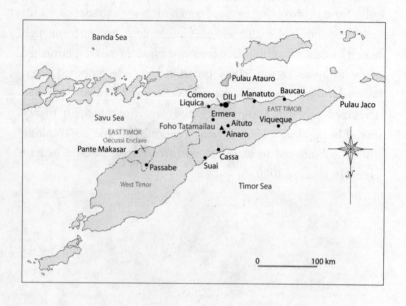

# TWO

# EAST TIMOR

## FEBRUARY 2000

## EAST TIMOR

In 1949, the Netherlands gave up its colonies in the Dutch West Indies, including West Timor, and the nation of Indonesia was born. East Timor remained under Portuguese control until winning independence on 28 November 1975. Indonesia responded by launching a full-scale military invasion, which continued until 1999, killing an estimated one third of the population. In January 1999, President B.J. Habibie unexpectedly announced that he was willing to hold a referendum on the question of East Timorese independence, reversing a quarter of a century of Indonesian rule. As the referendum on self-rule drew closer, fighting between separatist guerrillas and pro-Indonesian paramilitary forces in East Timor intensified. East Timorese militia groups armed by the Indonesian military systematically intimidated the population leading up to the popular referendum of 30 August 1999 sponsored by the United Nations. The sponsored referendum had to be rescheduled twice because of the violence.

Despite such intimidation, on 3 September the UN announced that the East Timorese had voted overwhelmingly in favour of independence from Indonesia: 98.6 per cent of registered voters went to the polls, with 78 per cent voting in favour of independence. In response, the attacks by the Indonesia-backed militia increased in intensity. In the ensuing bloodshed, an estimated fifteen hundred civilians were killed, others were raped and tortured and two hundred and fifty thousand were left homeless. The scale of the violence attracted international intervention. In October 1999, Operation Stabilise landed in East Timor. The 2300-strong International Force for East Timor (INTERFET) consisted mainly of Australian and New Zealand troops under the command of Major-General Peter Cosgrove.

As the UN C-130 Hercules approached the northeast coast of the island of Timor, I was able to catch a fleeting glance of the lush landscape and clear blue waters beneath us. The line from the television series *Mission Impossible* ran through my mind. Your mission, should you choose to accept it, is to go into East Timor and to perform autopsies on fifty-one bodies in three weeks. And now, here I was on a no-frills flight in a massive craft built to carry troops and equipment. Many of my fellow passengers wore the traditional and distinctive light blue shirts, blue caps and berets depicting the UN insignia. I was one of the handful of civilians. Earplugs had been distributed and I needed to wear them for the entire journey. The cabin smelled like a mechanic's garage with a mixture of humid air, body sweat and aviation fuel. It was dimly lit with few portholes and the seats were of moulded plastic with webbed seatbelts. The toilet was at the front of the cabin, with just a shower curtain pulled around it for privacy. Not surprisingly, I didn't see anybody use it. Just in case I wasn't already concerned about the chances of catching dengue fever, a newspaper cutting with the headline on the risk was taped to the bulkhead immediately in front of me. Once we reached altitude, the internal temperature dropped so much that fog and condensation dripped from the lagged pipes running the length of the ceiling of the fuselage. Beneath the newspaper cutting a notice advised: 'Get in, sit down, hang on and shut up'. I did just that.

The green expanse of dense jungle beneath us was interspersed with open fields and flashes of coastline. Occasionally I glimpsed a tall mountain with a river winding its way down. The sunlight reflecting off the rivers made them look silver. Details of the atrocities committed here jarred with the beauty of the scene unfolding beneath me. I knew there could very well be bodies buried in the areas we were flying over. John Hilton had vividly presented the massacre I was here to examine when he had approached the Victorian Institute of Forensic Medicine (VIFM) to call for volunteers to assist the international peacekeeping effort to East Timor.

## THE PASSABE MASSACRE

The story of what had become known as the Passabe massacre was horrifying. Passabe is a town just inside the coastal enclave in the southern part of Oecussi, 200 kilometres southwest of Dili. The enclave is a small patch of land belonging to East Timor, but it is actually located in West Timor. The area had been identified by militia groups as a pro-independence stronghold and was therefore a target for their violent pro-autonomy campaign. According to the testimony of the eyewitnesses who had survived the attack and escaped, members of the Indonesian military, militia groups and police were responsible for the massacre. On 9 September 1999, the militia groups allegedly moved along a road targeting pro-independence figures. They captured up to seventy young men from two villages in the town of Passabe, tied their hands and forced them into West Timor to register their names at a government building. They were then marched back across the border into the enclave. A shot was fired as a signal just as they had crossed a river. The men were then allegedly hacked to death with machetes in the early hours of 10 September. The militia groups ordered the local villagers to bury the bodies the next morning. For all I knew, we were flying over the spot where it had happened, or where similar events had occurred.

After an hour and a half, the Hercules began its thunderous descent. The temperature inside the aircraft rose uncomfortably, and I wondered what awaited me upon landing. My first mission to East Timor was conceived in the wake of the post-referendum destruction in the early days of January 2000. This was in response to a request from the United Nations (UN) in late 1999 for the international community to undertake forensic investigations into war crimes perpetrated in East Timor. While the extent of human rights violations was still being determined, mass graves and other evidence of massacres were surfacing throughout East Timor. Immediate assistance was needed to document the evidence necessary to secure convictions before it disappeared. Expressions of interest for foreign assistance were invited.

At that time, Professor John Hilton was the director of the New South Wales Institute of Forensic Medicine. Six members of his staff had volunteered to work in East Timor for the forensic division of the Special Crimes Investigation Unit (SCIU) set up by the United Nations Transitional Administration in East Timor (UNTAET). At the time, Øyvind Olsen was the director. The mandate of these units was to analyse crimes against humanity, war crimes and other serious violations of international humanitarian law. The forensic centre was to be staffed by experts from various countries who would rotate on a three-weekly basis. The New South Wales team had exhumed the bodies of the victims of the Passabe massacre. Although the exact number of victims was unknown, the remains of forty-nine victims had been recovered. The body bags awaited examination by an experienced forensic pathologist in a refrigerated container at the makeshift mortuary set up by the New South Wales team.

## CALL FOR VOLUNTEERS

John Hilton visited us at the VIFM and called a meeting to discuss the logistics of sending a forensic pathologist into East Timor to conduct these autopsies. At the meeting, he explained the situation. Sidney Jones, head of the human rights section of the UN and dedicated to the pursuit of human rights in East Timor, had related the details of the events surrounding the massacre to John. He described them vividly and showed us graphic images of the terrain and the facilities the forensic team would use. This massacre had been selected to be investigated because it was the worst single post-referendum massacre documented. Detailed statements had been obtained from the handful of survivors who had escaped, so this was also one of the better-documented atrocities. The perpetrators' whereabouts were known, so swift medico-legal examination of the bodies was required. It was of the utmost importance in prosecuting these crimes that the task of gathering and documenting this information be done by independent professionals. The role of the forensic staff would be to undertake full post-mortem examination of the remains exhumed and recovered from Passabe. The purpose of the forensic examination was to determine the cause and manner of death and identify the remains. This evidence would then be used in a court of law to prosecute the perpetrators. The bodies of the victims could then finally be returned to their families for a proper burial.

About a dozen staff attended the meeting, including the Director and Assistant Director, pathologists and technicians. After the meeting, John called for volunteers to carry out the post-mortem examinations. All of the staff present felt very much affected by the plight of the victims and their families—and indeed the East Timorese as a whole. Although I had been aware of the recent conflict in East Timor, I had not felt personally involved. But after hearing the details John gave us, I felt that if my skills could contribute to bringing the killers to justice then I wanted to go. I wanted to help bring some comfort and relief to the families of the victims. Such an investigation would also send a strong message to those who perpetrated such atrocities. If our work meant that they would be caught and punished for their actions in a court of law, perhaps it would serve as a warning that such crimes could not be committed with impunity.

The mission also posed a great professional and personal challenge for me. At that time, I had never examined the aftermath of a mass killing and my area of expertise was predominantly with the recently deceased. But I hoped that my skills as a forensic pathologist would equip me to undertake this mission successfully. After giving the matter some thought, and as I was able to leave whenever I was needed, I told Professor Stephen Cordner that I was interested.

## HEADING OFF INTO THE UNKNOWN

After a week or so, permission was granted through the UN. I signed a contract and travel arrangements were drawn up. Then I went through an excruciating bureaucratic process to get authorisation from the UN in New York. There were many faxes between John Hilton in Sydney and Sidney Jones and Ali Saleem in East Timor. Flights and arrangements were confirmed and cancelled and I started and abruptly ceased anti-malarial medication at least four times. Finally, everything was in order. On Sunday 13 February, several weeks after my expression of interest, I boarded the aircraft bound for Darwin, then Dili.

I left Melbourne with no idea of what awaited me in Dili. The original plan was that the VIFM would send a team of three: me as forensic pathologist, Associate Professor Christopher Briggs as physical anthropologist and Barry Murphy as mortuary technician. The permit papers for Chris and Barry were either denied or lost in the system, so I was on my way alone. For all I knew, I would be conducting the autopsies alone also. I hoped that I had packed everything that I would need and that I would be able to extend my skills to cover the work of the anthropologist and technician.

As we made our approach to the runway, Dili airport came into view. From the air, it resembled a scene out of the television show *MASH*. Even though the fighting was now under control, it still looked like a war zone. There were camouflaged fuel dumps, helicopters, armed troops, vehicles and other large military aircraft on the tarmac. It was then that it really hit me that I would be the first forensicpathologist to conduct autopsies on the victims of war crimes in the region. No forensic investigation on this scale had ever been undertaken in East Timor before. In addition to the possibility of staffing problems, I wasn't even sure that I could examine fifty-one bodies in three weeks. At home, I routinely perform three to four hundred autopsies a year. Of these, only twenty or so are due to homicide. I was only called upon to examine skeletal remains once or twice a year. Bodies in an advanced state of decomposition were more common. But it was too late for doubts now. Despite these feelings of trepidation and inadequacy, I would have to find ways and means to get the job done.

DILI

A blast of humid air greeted me as I took the first steps onto the terra firma of East Timor. After going through customs and immigration, I watched as the conveyer belt in the arrival hall roared into life and waited for what seemed like an eternity before my belongings appeared. In addition to my personal luggage, I had packed two large lockable blue plastic boxes containing all the basic autopsy equipment I could imagine needing. As I wasn't sure exactly what equipment and staff would be available, I had brought everything I thought I would need to complete the task alone. This included many pairs of surgical scrubs, rubber post-mortem gloves, gumboots and anthropological and standard post-mortem equipment. The anthropological essentials included vernier callipers and a measuring board to determine the length of the femur. These would be necessary for calculating the height of the individual. I'd also included charts with information on closure of epiphyses of bone, which were required to calculate age, and dental charts. Two of these charts remain on the mortuary wall to this day.

Because of the debacle leading up to my departure for East Timor, I was very concerned that lines of communication may have failed and that nobody would be at the airport to collect me. After dragging the two large boxes and my personal possessions out to the side of the airport, I was pleasantly surprised to see a young man standing there holding up a piece of cardboard with my name on it. This was Matthew Skinner, the son of Mark Skinner, an eminent physical anthropologist from Canada. Matt was a volunteer with the UN and had been present during the exhumations at the Oecussi enclave. I was very relieved to have someone meet me, but even more so to find that I would have the help of an anthropologist after all. We loaded the luggage onto an open-tray 4WD UN vehicle in the scorching heat, and headed towards the mortuary to examine the facilities and discuss the plans for the fifty-one post-mortem examinations we would be undertaking in a few days. Forty-nine of these were the victims of the Passabe massacre. There was one further body bag from Atabe and another from Liquica.

## THE MORTUARY

The mortuary was located at Comoro, about a ten-minute drive from the airport. We drove along the sealed road that ran the length of Dili from the airport to the centre of town. The surroundings were beautiful. To my left was the beach and to my right, intense green mountains. The sky was blue and the air was warm and humid. We travelled past several small hotels and open park areas. Roadside stalls sold tropical fruit, cigarettes and plastic bottles filled with petrol. Open-tray trucks full of people and small cars with doors and windows missing sped along the potholed roads with a total disregard for any road rules. There were no traffic lights. At one intersection, a policeman was trying to control the traffic, but nobody paid any attention to him. Burnt-out vehicles littered the roadside.

As we got closer to the city, the comparatively tranquil scenery was replaced by scenes of the aftermath of war. The fires of Dili had long been extinguished, but the degree of destruction made it seem that it could have ended just yesterday. The city had been almost completely destroyed by the Indonesian-backed militia groups who had selected the homes of pro-independence supporters in an alarmingly precise and deliberate fashion. The largest buildings had obviously been targeted, but many of the smaller buildings had been systematically burnt. These ruins were interspersed with untouched houses in perfect condition; apparently they belonged to those families sympathetic to the Indonesian-backed autonomy forces. Matt explained that he had heard of trucks carrying tanks of accelerant that the militia groups sprayed onto the buildings owned by pro-independence sympathisers before setting them alight.

The arrival of the International Force for East Timor (INTERFET) troops in September 1999 stopped the destructive forces of the militia groups who had been active since late August of that year. By then, though, the majority of buildings had been burnt to the ground. Some of the larger, statelier buildings were still standing, but had been completely gutted by fire. Occupants had cleared the debris out and huge piles of concrete and miscellaneous burnt material lay inside and out the front of these buildings. The strong smell of smoke pervaded the city.

As we drove, Matt told me about the exhumations. As he had been part of the operation, he was able to give me an accurate description of the condition of the bodies at the time of discovery. The exhumations had taken place some four months after the time of the massacre. Dr Allan Cala, a very proficient forensic pathologist from New South Wales, had coordinated the exhumation team, which was composed of members of the New South Wales forensic team, INTERFET troops and UN officials. Observers, including family members, were also present. They were very welcoming and eager to see justice done.

From what Matt told me, the exhumations at the Passabe site had been a difficult business. Using picks, shovels and sieves for the small bones and personal items, the team began digging up the identified graves. Scorpions were everywhere. Some of the bodies were buried near the surface and some were in deep graves. Most of the bodies were buried one or two to a grave. Other skeletal remains were just picked up off the ground where they were littering the sides of the hills; they had probably been scavenged by animals. The team also found several incomplete sets of human remains, which they sent to the morgue at Dili. Two more bodies, buried in quicksand, could not be retrieved. Up to eight others were believed to be in graves in West Timor, within sight, but out of legal reach of the team.

After exhumation, the bodies were placed in body bags and tagged with the GPS location to indicate precisely where they were found. The operation was delayed by security concerns and heavy rains, so it was not until 6 February after six days work that the job was complete. Five months after the killings, it was time for the proper investigation into these murders. All was now in readiness for the final stage of the investigation. After my team had done our work, the prosecution could proceed. I was now ready for what I would come to regard as the single most important professional experience of my life.

The car took an immediate right turn into a large complex of buildings. A weathered sign out the front indicated that this was the Agricultural College of Dili. A security guard met us at the gate and ushered us through. We proceeded up the driveway on the left side of the complex and a large refrigerated container came into view. This container was like any on a wharf or factory site, except that the contents of this one were fifty-one body bags.

Before we began the autopsies, we had set a couple of days aside to prepare. First we checked out the buildings we would be working in for the next few weeks. Before its targeted destruction by the militia, the Agricultural College of Dili had been an impressive complex. The buildings were long rectangular structures, all with tin roofs and highly polished white porcelain tile floors. Three buildings ran more or less parallel to the road and were intersected by covered walkways. The building closest to the road was largely vacant. Members of the SCIU occupied the second building and the third housed the mortuary facility. A further two or three buildings towards the back of the complex were completely destroyed. Behind a few small outbuildings stood a large ornate building with columns at the portico, which was completely deserted and scattered with dust, dirt and debris.

The mortuary building consisted of the post-mortem room. Next to this was a vacant room. In the room next to that, six INTERFET soldiers had set up their base. Their office had computers, maps on the wall, rations and a refrigerator full of Coca-Cola. Shayne Towers-Hammond was based there, with about half a dozen others, including Wayne Fee. Shayne became an indispensable member of our team and Wayne was to become a good personal friend during my subsequent visits to East Timor. He was originally a Victorian police officer and army reservist. He went to East Timor with the first contingent of INTERFET and then shed the army uniform and became a full-time employee of the SCIU. He lived there until 2004 when he met and married an Australian who was also working in East Timor.

As I was the first of the rotating international forensic pathologists to arrive to conduct post-mortem examinations, I was a bit apprehensive about the adequacy of the facilities and equipment that would be available. I was pleased to find that the facilities and conditions were more than adequate. The college had been well chosen as the site for the mortuary by the New South Wales forensic team. I imagine that this choice was largely based on the fact that it was an intact building with a washable floor, water supply and reasonably reliable power supply. The Asia Foundation had donated facilities and equipment for the forensic centre and the New South Wales team had cleared away the debris before we arrived. The team had installed air-conditioning units and they had improvised by making the autopsy tables out of wooden trestle tables topped by stainless steel refrigeration trays. There was another large wooden trestle table on the opposite side of the room, which we would use for our cameras, autopsy pro-formas and other things. This table was pretty rickety. When one of the INTERFET soldiers leaned on it, it tipped over, scattering our gear in all directions. Rubber non-skid mats had been laid out on the floor between the tables to provide a relatively safe workplace. A small room with a sink at the back of the building served as our changeroom, a washroom for the instruments and a storeroom for our gumboots and scrubs.

This set-up far exceeded my expectations, and I felt reassured. I had anticipated working from a small ramshackle building somewhere in the outskirts of the city. I thought I might only have my two plastic boxes of equipment to work with. I certainly didn't envisage the added luxuries of running water and air-conditioning.

Once I had made sure that all the necessities were there, I went to explore the rest of the college campus. The buildings towards the back were completely gutted, exposing the wanton destruction of the militia. As I walked from room to room, I could see trashed office equipment, files, pamphlets, photographic negatives, masses of broken glass and charred debris everywhere. Books from the library and students' academic records with photographs, subjects studied and grades were scattered about on the floor. It was eerie to walk through this area of destruction with only the crunching sound of broken glass beneath my feet. I felt strange, almost as if I was being observed. Occasionally a large rat would scuttle across the room, giving me a start. One room contained a small, heavy metal safe, which had been blown apart by explosives. Its twisted door was testimony to the militia's intention to steal any valuables that may have been housed there. I took many photos of these destroyed parts of the building.

Despite my positive impression of the morgue set-up, and although many others shared the facility with us, there was a strong sense of desolation about the place. The irony of the purpose of the college compared to what it was now being used for did not escape me. As I walked through the trashed and deserted rooms, I wondered briefly whether any of the young men lying dead in the container next to what was now the mortuary may have hoped to attend this college one day. I didn't dwell on this thought.

Although we had been allocated three weeks to accomplish the examination of the bodies, I was afraid that this timeframe was going to be cut short by one week. Just before my departure, I had been informed that the Supreme Court in Melbourne would be hearing a significant murder trial on the Monday of my third week in Timor and, in spite of many phone calls and faxes to the Department of Public Prosecutions in Melbourne, it looked as though I would have to attend this court case in person. When forensic pathologists are abroad, colleagues are often able to represent them in court, especially when the case is straightforward. A bullet wound to the head or multiple stab wounds are self-evident causes of death in a homicide case. But in this case, my opinion was pivotal. It was a particularly complex example of blunt force trauma and asphyxiation and could not be represented by anyone else. This would mean we would have a little over two weeks to accomplish three weeks' work.

I thought about the job that lay ahead and weighed up the likelihood that we would be able to succeed with the entire task given the time constraints. We would have to document all observable injuries, reconstruct the skeletal elements and attempt to identify any distinguishing features found during the course of the examination. Despite my minimal experience with decomposed or skeletal remains, I was optimistic that my background would provide sufficient grounding for the job ahead. But the time constraints meant I wasn't so sure of myself. At home, the discovery of a skeleton is an uncommon event and pathologists have the luxury of consulting a physical anthropologist towards the end of the examination. In many ways, the examination of skeletal elements at home is easy, as the initial examination can be performed in several hours and then the remains handed over to the skeleton experts for final arbitration. At home, time constraints were rarely an issue. In East Timor, they were very real, as every case was an individual example of horrendous homicide and we could take no shortcuts.

On the positive side, the task of identifying the cause of death should be fairly straightforward. We had eyewitness evidence that the majority of these victims had been hacked to death with machetes. Our investigations should confirm the details of this eyewitness evidence. Despite the level of decomposition and even though I had been warned that some of the bags contained no more than a couple of bones, I hoped the remains would provide adequate clues as to the cause of death. Also, the examination of decomposed bodies and skeletons requires little more than a sharp scalpel, a good stout pair of dissecting scissors and a pair of toothed forceps. The rest of the examination was hands-on processing of the bones and extraction of all evidential material. I was familiar with the procedures and the equipment, so I felt that I just had to plunge in and do my best. The workload could be got through with many long days and extended work hours.

After our visit to the mortuary, we next visited the UN compound where I was to meet Sidney Jones. I was even more struck during this twenty-minute drive by the complete devastation and carnage perpetrated by the militia groups on the people and property of Dili. Most of the city had been devastated; the site brought to mind the photographs of Hiroshima after the atom bomb was dropped. That was the only point of comparison I had for the annihilation I saw. The INTERFET troops had gauged the degree of destruction as near a hundred per cent. It was obviously the result of a scorched earth policy—virtually nothing had been spared. There were a few people around, but not what you would expect in a capital city. Not many shops were open for business, as most had been destroyed. Some outdoor stalls had been set up and blue tarpaulins were acting as makeshift roofs over many of the buildings. There were two restaurants in operation, one of which was called The Burnt House for obvious reasons. I understand it is still called that today. A couple of small hotels offered basic accommodation.

As I was taking in the surroundings with some difficulty, Matt told me some horror stories he had heard from the INTERFET troops he worked with during the Passabe exhumation. The militia had even sprayed rice paddy fields with kerosene. The level of destruction appeared to ease off out into the outskirts of Dili, though the pattern of intact and destroyed houses standing side by side extended right to the point where the UN compound began.

At the time of my first mission, the UN compound was a heavily guarded school complex. This site was itself the scene of a significant shooting incident during the conflict. Many of the UN staff had pulled out of the area because the fighting was becoming too intense. When the militia stormed the school, some staff took refuge in the buildings. Others escaped over the high back fence and into the hills behind. I believe some people were shot and killed. The first building now housed the UN human rights section, where Sidney waited for me.

Sidney is a tall, lanky American with an intense passion for human rights and a phenomenal work ethic. She has a reputation for telling it like it is and was later expelled from Jakarta for her outspoken views. She was heading up the International Crisis Group at the time and the official reason given for her expulsion was passport irregularities. We were friends immediately. She was very excited about me performing the medico-legal examination of the bodies from Passabe and we discussed the logistics of how to get through the cases in the allotted time. She told me that she would attempt to have me relieved of my court duties in Melbourne, but she wasn't successful. Throughout the mission, Sidney was invaluable in providing me with whatever assistance I needed on any matter.

## SETTLING IN

I had arrived with no idea of where to find accommodation for the duration of my stay, as this had not been previously discussed nor arranged. I asked Sidney how I should best go about looking and she very graciously offered her small house. We agreed to meet later the same day so that I could settle in and unpack. I then underwent my UN induction. This only took about an hour and a half and went quite smoothly. This was to change for the worst in subsequent missions. All I was required to do on this first mission was to fill out several forms and have my photograph taken so I could access secure areas and pass freely from place to place with minimal delay. I organised a time to have a jab for Japanese encephalitis. I was already fully immunised against hepatitis, tetanus, polio and several other infections that were rife in Timor. I decided against the vaccination for rabies, as I had heard that the side effects of this injection were more unpleasant than the disease itself.

Then it was time to head off to Sidney's house in Lhani, a small suburb approximately twenty minutes' drive from the mortuary facility. We drove along narrow unmade roads full of pedestrians, bicycles, dogs and children. I was surprised at the children's happy faces, which seemed at such odds with the burnt-out surroundings. When the car moved slowly, we would slap 'high fives' out the window with the local children. I saw extensive destruction of houses and buildings. The house where Sidney lived was at the end of a long, steep driveway, against the backdrop of tall hills and palm trees. To the immediate right of this was a tall stone fence, which led to a Jesuit compound. The militia had left untouched the small series of buildings belonging to an extended family. I was later to learn that the owner of the building had been on a death list and her home would certainly have been razed to the ground by the militia, given time. The family didn't speak English, so we communicated with sign language. They seemed happy to have us there, and they were paid a small amount to cover the costs of keeping us.

Sidney showed me to my lodgings, a small sparsely furnished bedroom towards the back area of the house. I gratefully noted the flywire screens across the windows and an upright pedestal fan. There was a small refrigerator, which Sidney had thoughtfully stocked with beer. The bed was a single mattress on the floor with a light sheet and there was a chair in the corner of the room. That was about it. The remainder of the building was essentially the same.

The family were very friendly; they provided a laundry service and prepared our meals. The meals were to be simple and unvarying. Breakfast would usually be a dry bread roll and black coffee, lunch would be noodles and dinner would be a rice dish, perhaps with some fish, and fruit for dessert. Everything was very simple, but adequate. Out the back was a rather spartan toilet and washing facility. The toilet was non-flushable and toilet paper had to be placed in a nearby container for disposal. The bathing facility consisted of an upright tile-lined dip tub. The water came directly from the mountains and was freezing. I was instantly awake after washing in the mornings. The relief from the heat was short-lived, though. I'd no sooner towel myself off than I'd be drenched in sweat again.

After settling in and unpacking my gear, I spent the rest of the afternoon walking around the suburb of Lhani and taking photographs. It was a rather strange sensation walking through the streets of war-torn East Timor and I felt rather conscious of the fact that I was wearing reasonably good clothing and carried an expensive camera. This was in stark contrast to my surroundings, which showed so much devastation and despair. In spite of this, the local children came up to me and shook my hand with the standard greeting of 'Hello, mister!' They had charming smiles and showed no apprehension in approaching a visiting westerner. I took photos of some of the children, who giggled and posed for me happily. Their beautiful smiles seemed unaffected by the ruins surrounding them.

Many of the buildings that had been left standing were covered in graffiti. The word *merdeka* was painted on several of the larger buildings and fences. Apparently this word means independence. On several other fences there was an extended message in a language that I could not identify. Perhaps it was Tetun or Bahasa Indonesian. The literal translation of this message was 'This is what we got for making a wrong decision—goodbye East Timor'. These messages, scrawled on the walls of burnt-out and abandoned buildings contributed to the sense of utter desolation. The atmosphere was like that of a ghost town and yet people lived on in the aftermath of the attacks, going about their daily business amid the ruins. It was difficult to reconcile what I was seeing with my lifestyle and environment at home in Melbourne.

The military presence on this first mission to East Timor was enormous. During my short trip around the area, I saw several out-of-uniform soldiers taking their exercise. They were dressed in shorts and t-shirts and jogged along the road drenched in sweat. Army regulations meant that they had to be armed at all times and it was a strange sight to see them jogging while carrying semi-automatic rifles or pistols. Trucks of soldiers being transported from place to place passed by regularly. These soldiers wore the characteristic camouflage uniforms and were fully armed. During the first mission, I never felt threatened at any stage. This was partly due to the military presence, but also because of the welcoming attitude of the locals. They looked up to UN staff and seemed to regard Australians in particular almost reverentially. This would change in following missions, particularly my last one to East Timor in December 2002. I think this was because things had not improved very much for the locals. They were lacking even the most basic of essentials, while the westerners had lots of American dollars to spend and drove around in new 4WDs, having fun at local restaurants and bars.

After walking through the ruined town, I wanted to get started on my work as soon as possible. Even though my contribution to restoring order and justice would be comparatively small, it would help bring some justice to the victims.

Sidney arrived back at the lodgings that evening in time to share a short meal of a spiced rice dish. After this, we unpacked and assembled several cartons of prefabricated furniture that had been bought for the house. It consisted of multiple planks and tubular structures all fitting together with bolts and Allen keys. This process took several hours by torchlight (the power had failed that evening), and we had quite a few laughs.

Time was passing quickly. The following morning was day three of the mission. After a breakfasting on a dry bread roll and black coffee (which I eventually got used to), Sidney dropped me off at the mortuary. I unpacked, prepared the autopsy equipment and put the charts up on the walls. Then I noticed the overgrowth of vegetation in the centre of the buildings in what used to be a garden area. All that was left of the garden was a now defunct fountain and the remains of an elaborate grapevine. As the area had been neglected during the past few months, the grass had grown until it was about a metre high, providing a perfect breeding ground for mosquitoes. The thought of dengue fever was always in my mind. This mosquito-borne disease strikes at random and can be fatal. Other than taking basic precautions, such as using insect repellent and keeping away from stagnant water, there is little that can be done for protection. During my stay, there were approximately ten cases of dengue fever reported, some of which resulted in death, including that of a UN staff member. As much work was required to reduce the mosquito population in the immediate area, we organised some of the locals to cut the grass. This took them a day or so as there were no lawn mowers or brushcutters. Instead they used the ubiquitous machete or jungle knife to cut the grass down till it was a few centimetres high. In the days to come, we would see only too clearly the damage the machete could inflict when used as a weapon of war.

After I had settled in, Sidney came out to the morgue and we discussed further the plans for the following days. I was hoping to get through five cases a day and to write the reports at the end of each working day. Sidney strongly recommended that I take a trip to Liquica, a small township about an hour and a half away. It was the site of a notorious church massacre that had been highly publicised. One of the soldiers agreed to drive me and we headed off to the west of Dili along the coastal road. When we arrived, the soldier introduced me to the local police commander in the centre of town. The commander was gracious enough to give me half an hour of his time and related the dreadful events that had occurred at the Liquica church in April 1999. Militia, soldiers and police allegedly attacked hundreds of refugees sheltering in the Catholic church after slaughtering several civilians nearby the day before. Up to two hundred people hiding in the church had been murdered. According to some sources, the number killed was around sixty, but information gained by the locals, in particular the nuns, suggested that the number was closer to one hundred and seventy-five people or more. Witnesses stated that bodies were piled high on at least five trucks to be taken away for disposal.

The police commander also showed me several large maps attached to the wall of his office. Large numbers of small black pins indicated mass gravesites and sites of body disposals. The map was of the Liquica area only and the number of pins on it horrified me. He also told me of a lake nearby where bodies had been dumped and where scattered bones were sometimes found along the shore. Other information told of bodies that had been dumped in wells and others into the sea from helicopters. This was just one fraction of the total number of atrocities perpetrated in East Timor. Due to the absence of an accurate population census, the true numbers will never be known, but it has been estimated that several thousand people were killed up to and immediately after the referendum vote. It was a very sobering visit, but I was glad I went as it helped put into context the work that lay ahead of me.

Returning to the UN compound later that day, I met Ali Saleem, a co-worker of Sidney's in the human rights section. Ali, a very energetic, driven person, had been integral to my coming to East Timor and had put in a great effort to get the mission underway. He and others had been disappointed by the lack of swift intervention by a forensic group in the early days, but we all agreed that this was a complex process and had to be approached with tact and discretion. He was very relieved that the process was finally underway. When I told Ali that I would be required for the trial in the Supreme Court before the three weeks was up, he also unsuccessfully attempted to intervene with the Department of Public Prosecutions. After the time spent on the initial set-up, we would have ten working days to examine the bodies.

## GETTING STARTED

On day four of the mission, the preparations were complete and we were finally ready to open the refrigerated container. It was linked to the power supply by cables, but Matt had warned me that the power supply in Dili was intermittent at best. In the two weeks since the bodies had been stored in the container, the refrigerator had been continuously turning itself on and off. This resulted in extended putrefaction of the contained bodies, as the temperatures inside fluctuated between –10°C and 50°C, instead of remaining stable at +4°C. Approximately five months had elapsed between the burials and the exhumations and although the doors of the container were firmly clamped shut and padlocked, the sickly sweet stench of decay emanated from it.

I thought I had pretty much seen it all during my work at the VIFM and thought myself difficult to shock. In my four years as a forensic pathologist, I had regularly been confronted with the worst that people are capable of doing to each other. Yet it was with some apprehension that I walked towards the container of bodies. As we opened the doors, a blast of putrid air hit us. Body bags covered the entire floor and were unceremoniously stacked to half fill the room-sized container. Some of the body bags looked full and some looked almost empty. I had never seen so many dead bodies together at one time; nothing in my previous experience had prepared me for what I saw. The container full of body bags is a memory that will stay with me forever.

I took a moment, and then, with a deep breath, Matt and I stepped into the container. We picked up the nearest body bag and carried it through the walkway to the mortuary. It weighed practically nothing. As we walked, the full impact of just how much the task ahead exceeded anything I had previously undertaken hit me. While the sight of the contents of the container had momentarily taken me aback, I quickly became more strongly determined to restore some dignity to these young men and return them to their families for a proper burial. Even though our timeframe was now reduced by a third, and despite less than optimal conditions, we would help to bring about justice and accountability for these murders.

At least we were a team of three by this time. The team consisted of me as forensic pathologist and Matt Skinner as physical anthropologist. Matt would also act as mortuary manager and would be responsible for logging the bodies in and out of the refrigerator and mortuary. Matt was an enthusiastic worker and had volunteered to undertake a tour of duty with the UN in East Timor. Technically, he had not yet qualified as a physical anthropologist, as he had one further year of training to do back in Canada. This meant his work would need to be checked further down the line. Despite this, his work proved to be outstanding and his findings were later entirely confirmed. One of the INTERFET soldiers, Shayne Towers-Hammond, was assigned to be our scene-of-crime officer and photographer. Shayne is an Australian soldier with a distinguished military career. He was more than willing to assist with anything we asked of him and more. This job was not for the faint-hearted and it was certainly not within his brief to perform the duties that would be required, but Matt and I were very grateful for his assistance. Matt was quiet and reserved and Shayne was extroverted and affable. We all got on wonderfully, which was absolutely essential in such a small team. My fears of having to get through this alone were allayed. As to whether we could get it done by the deadline remained to be seen. If we could get through at least five or six examinations a day then we could complete the caseload.

As Matt had been present at the exhumations, I relied on him heavily to advise me on how best to proceed through the contents of the container. He thought that the bodies could be examined in any order, as the majority of them were moderately to severely decomposed. Skeletal remains predominated. He warned me that there was one bag that should be examined last. It was of considerable weight compared to the others and would therefore require more intensive attention. The body bags were all numbered and labelled according to where the remains had been found.

## THE AUTOPSIES

I was ready to open the first body bag. Due to its light weight, and from what Matt had told me to expect, I suspected that it contained no more than a few bones of one of the poor unfortunates who had died on that night at Passabe. As I unzipped the bag, I was confronted with a sticky mass of soil mixed with decomposed soft tissue. Upon closer examination, I could make out bones and clothing fragments encased in the mixture of mud and decomposing flesh. In spite of a small amount of adhering decomposing tissue, this body was technically skeletonised. I got a shock at the sight of a white gleaming skull that had been meticulously cleaned, contrasting starkly with the rest of the contents of the bag. Dr Christopher Griffiths, a forensic odontologist from New South Wales, had charted the dental records of the victims before my forensic examination. No further examination had been performed up until this time.

From a professional perspective, I anticipated that identification and documentation of the injuries on bodies would be relatively straightforward. There was no mystery surrounding the way these men had come about their deaths. The majority of victims from Passabe had been hacked to death with machetes. The machete is a jungle knife carried by virtually everybody for use in a variety of daily activities. As a weapon it is deadly. The forty-centimetre curved blade is heavy and sharp, and can inflict terrible injuries. I anticipated that some trace of the injuries inflicted would be recognisable on the bones. Our aim was to identify and document all signs of injury, and ultimately to establish definitely the cause of death of each victim. According to documentation gathered on the slaughter, all the bodies to be examined (with the exception of the children) were young adult males, many between eighteen and twenty-five years old. I found this aspect of the cases particularly difficult, as I have children of a similar age. I couldn't even imagine being in the position of their parents and families.

In addition to identifying the cause of death, we were to document the anthropological characteristics of age, sex and height to help with identification. So that any evidential material with the skeletal remains remained intact, I had to examine the contents of the bag before anything else was done. The presence of a ligature, perhaps surrounding the forearms, may be vitally important to the interpretation of a case. It may show that the victim had been tied up and was therefore a defenceless non-combatant at the time of death. If the ligature became separated from the skeleton, then its importance would be diminished. This type of material could be in a very fragile condition by the time we got to examine the bodies and I had to handle them with great care so as not to inadvertently destroy evidence.

Next I removed the clothing from the skeletal remains and dirt. Contrary to what I was expecting, the t-shirt disclosed multiple small, round, two- or three-millimetre circular defects through the upper mid back and right shoulder area. The pattern of these holes was consistent with the scatter of shotgun pellets. Shayne told me that the use of firearms in East Timor was distinctly uncommon and it was a surprise to see this on examining the very first body. I was particularly interested in this evidence, as one of my areas of expertise is in gunshot wounds and I was puzzled by the pattern of injuries. I later found out that they were due to the discharge of rather crude homemade weapons known as *rakitans*, which fire small fragments of rock, glass or metal.

Next we separated the bones from the mud and decomposed matter and placed them in a pile ready for cleaning. Shayne, Matt and I then took a pile of bones each. We cleaned them using a bucket of water and scrubbing brush and laid them out to dry. This took no more than twenty minutes. After we had removed all the residual soil and decomposing matter from the body bag, we scanned it with a metal detector and then took it out the back to sift it so that any small objects that could provide a clue to the identity of the body would be separated. It would be disastrous to miss evidence such as a projectile, small bones or teeth, or distinctive personal items such as jewellery. We needed a quarter-inch sieve for this, but there was nothing like that in the mortuary, nor had I thought to bring one with me. I went searching among the debris towards the back of the complex and found a fragment of a window frame containing mesh, which was close to a quarter inch. This proved to be an excellent substitute until a formal examination sieve was produced several days later.

The next setback was when we tried to get running water to sieve the remains. The pressure was so low that it only trickled through the hose. It took half an hour or more to sieve a couple of kilograms of loose soil. Making our frustration worse, we sweated so profusely in the extreme heat and humidity that our insect repellent poured off as soon as we applied it. While we sieved through the sticky mess, both hands occupied with the bucket, sieve and hose, mosquitoes descended upon us in great numbers. Swatting them was impossible, so we carried on sieving while they feasted on us and tried our best to ignore unwelcome thoughts of contracting malaria or dengue fever or both.

Once the bones were dry, Matt assembled them in anatomical position to work out the person's age, gender and height. This skeleton was incomplete: the right forearm, left upper and lower arm, both hands and both feet were missing. Matt faithfully recorded all these features, noting the missing skeletal elements in an anthropological pro-forma. Once he had done this, it was time to search for evidence of the injuries that had caused death.

I examined the cranium of the deceased person. This revealed no apparent abnormalities. The teeth had been previously cleaned and examined by the forensic odontologist. There was prominent betel-nut juice staining on all of the teeth. We found this in virtually all of the bodies examined. Betel nut chewing is part of the culture of Polynesia and Melanesia, including East Timor. Matt and I then meticulously examined every bone in an attempt to identify any sign of injury that would be left by a cutting instrument, gunshot or blunt trauma. Upon close examination, we noted several deep incised or cutting defects through the upper spine. These injuries were the telltale sign of the hacking action of a machete as the killer had attempted to decapitate the body. If this was not sufficiently horrifying, a further examination of the injuries on the arm and leg bones clearly showed that the reason the forearms and feet were missing from the bag was because they had been hacked off. Shayne photographed and logged all bones once evidence of injury had been identified. These were kept aside for evidence in the legal proceedings.

I concluded from my examination of the injuries that the cause of death of this first victim was a single shotgun blast to the back in combination with deeply incised cutting injuries to the neck. In other words, he had been shot, dismembered and had his throat cut. We were to come across a similar pattern of injuries again and again as we progressed through the bodies in the container. It didn't need much imagination to picture the torture inflicted upon these unfortunate individuals in the bloodbath that led up to their deaths. They were defenceless, many were bound, and they surely endured indescribable terror watching as their brothers, cousins and friends were butchered in front of them before it was their turn.

As we were finding our way through unknown territory, this first case took several hours to complete. I wrote up the report by hand after we concluded the autopsy. In the report, I included the results of the external examination—height, gender, description of clothing, degree of decomposition and accurate documentation of all injuries in bones and soft tissue. I then wrote a conclusion and comment regarding the mechanism of death. We created body maps to illustrate the location of all the injuries we had identified. Once I had completed the report, I signed it and Matt attached his anthropological report. This documented which bones were present, which were missing, areas of injury and the anthropological assessment of height, gender and age of the deceased. It was important to crosscheck our notes at the end of each case so that we could add any anomalies or afterthoughts before we forgot them. When we had finished, the reports would be handed in as documentary evidence to the SCIU.

We moved on to the second case of the day, following the same procedure. We would use this procedure for each of the fifty-one cases. The injuries we found on this body proved to be more typical of the cases that we saw over the following ten days. Once again, there was clear evidence of incised injuries to the throat area, though this time they were concentrated around the jaw. In a pattern that was to become more and more familiar, there were also multiple incised injuries to the ribs. The evidence of these wounds showed that the assailant had stabbed and slashed the victim with the jungle knife around the neck and ribs. The resulting injuries were horrendous, and even worse, they would not necessarily have been immediately lethal.

The third case was very similar to the first two, though I found a simple crossover ligature about his wrists. This ligature had been fashioned from a length of camouflage material. Examination of further bodies throughout the following days disclosed ligatures fashioned from all manner of materials ranging from jungle vine to wire and conventional rope. The cause of death of this last case of the day was a single deep machete blow to the left side of the head and jaw, which appeared to be the result of a single strike only. The body was largely incomplete, so I could make no comment about other causes of death.

By the end of the first working day, we had examined the contents of three body bags. Despite the gruelling nature of the work, completing the examination of these three victims was enormously satisfying to the team. The technique that we had developed as a matter of trial and error worked quite well. Unlike forensic work at home, the division of duties within the team were often blurred, with all of us mucking in with whatever needed to be done. Shayne was happy to help with cleaning bones and clothing and Matt didn't mind the onerous chore of washing and drying bones before laying them out for examination. It was very dirty work—mud and decomposing matter was spread throughout the building by the time we had completed the first day. We all cleaned up the mortuary, washing the floor down with soap and water, wiping the benches and arranging the instruments for the next day. We cleared away the pile of Coke cans and water bottles that had formed during the day.

As we cleaned, I thought about whether we were likely to achieve our goal. Although our system was working well, we would have to work faster to complete the forty-eight cases in the nine remaining working days. We worked very well together as a team and had developed a routine. Despite the shortcomings of the equipment and facilities, I felt that we would become more efficient in the days that followed. I had initially been concerned that we lacked an x-ray machine to identify bullets and projectiles in the body before I examined them. But this didn't cause as much of a problem as it could have as the majority of killings were done with jungle knives and their legacy was immediately apparent on examination. Although I still felt the pressure of the deadline, I felt much more positive that what we had set out to do was actually achievable.

The only problem with the equipment made available for the autopsies was that the trestle tables were a little too high for the initial examination of the body bags. They were suitable for examining the skeleton once it was assembled, but we had to undo the body bags, wash the bones and extract the evidentiary material while kneeling on the floor. This didn't take long, thankfully, but after several examinations I felt the effect of the hard polished tile floor against my knees and had to find something soft to kneel on. Once we had separated the individual bones into buckets for washing, reassembly was a relatively easy matter to deal with because we could work standing at the tables. The intermittent electricity supply created further delays and difficulties, but the air-conditioning was quite effective, not so much in cooling the air, but in moving it around the rather large open room.

The first day showed us that we wouldn't have a problem determining the anthropological characteristics of the victims, but individual identification was going to be problematic. Few of the bodies had any form of identification on them. Although Chris Griffiths had performed meticulous dental examinations on the skulls of the victims, the victims had little or no dental work done and few dental records were kept or had survived the conflict in East Timor. Further compounding the problem, very few photographs existed of those who had died. So the most practical method of preliminary identification was through clothing. Any pathologist will tell you that this falls well below the accepted minimum for identification procedures. But, far from ideal as it was, this method in fact proved to be quite effective.

Because of the hot and humid climate, the locals wear very light clothing. Most of the victims were clothed only in a pair of shorts and a t-shirt. Curiously, I never saw one t-shirt that matched another. As no two t-shirts had the same design, this meant that they could be a unique identifier. The pairs of shorts seemed to be distinctive also. Several of the bodies of young men wore shorts with numbers sewn on them. It turned out that they played on the same soccer team. It would be the surviving relatives' sad duty to identify their sons from the numbers sewn onto their soccer shorts. We did not take part in the process of identification, but we did prepare the clothing and photographs for the relatives to make tentative identifications at a later stage. While this technique was not scientific and would not have satisfied a court of law, it helped bring closure to the relatives of the victims. DNA was to be taken from the relatives at this later stage and compared with DNA taken from the teeth and bones of the deceased.

Most of the bodies were in an advanced state of decomposition, so examining the clothes also provided the best clues as to the type of injuries sustained. In some instances there was a pattern in the clothes indicating gunshots, but I found no bullets or damage on the remains. So all the clothes had to be washed, dried and fully examined for the telltale signs of bullets or knives. As they were in a state of extreme degradation, this had to be done with great care. To do this, we needed something to serve as a washing bucket. We looked around but couldn't find anything appropriate. The most likely looking containers were the blue plastic boxes that I'd brought my equipment in, so I decided to give one up for a washing bucket. Shayne became the laundry person and at the end of the day he emptied the fine black-brown offensive silt that had accumulated at the bottom of the box outside the building among the rest of the debris that had accumulated over time. When the clothes began to accumulate, we decided to use a vacant room just off the mortuary as a laundry. The room was quite small, but had the advantage of having barred windows on either side. Shayne rigged up a string for the clothesline and pegged the clothes up to dry and also to make it easy to examine them further. The smell in the small room was nauseating. Even though Shayne had cleaned the clothing as well as possible, the smell of the decomposing matter that had adhered to the clothes was even stronger than in the autopsy room. He photographed, logged, bagged and tagged the evidential items, personal property and clothing once it had been washed and dried. We noted the brand, size and description of the clothing and charted any defects before putting them in a paper bag and storing them for later use as evidence and for identification.

I was pleased that we had managed to get a workable system up and running in the makeshift mortuary, and with our progress. I was so exhausted by the end of the day that I fell asleep quickly. But in the early morning I was woken by severe abdominal pain. I had begun taking anti-malarial medication before I left Australia and was meant to continue taking it while in East Timor and for several weeks after returning home. Side effects were common and include nausea, vomiting, diarrhoea and skin rashes. That night, the side effects took their toll. As I hastily made my way to the toilet at the back of the house, I wondered whether nausea and the subsequent dehydration would prevent me from continuing the following nine days' work. If I stopped taking the medication, I risked contracting malaria. Neither prospect facing me was appealing. But despite the risk, and because of the debilitating side effects I was suffering, I decided to stop the medication. If I had continued taking it, I would have been physically incapable of continuing with the workload. I chose to take my chances with the mosquitoes.

The nausea and diarrhoea settled down after a few days, though I was able to take little in the way of solid food. I took anti-diarrhoeal medication and needed water frequently. The UN provided unlimited quantities of bottled spring water and it was common for me to drink ten litres a day. I still felt that I bordered on dehydration because of the heat, the humidity and the hard physical work. As fast as we drank, we sweated it off. The air-conditioning unit was working virtually non-stop and at the end of the day the 44-gallon drums beneath the collecting pipe were filled with water. This brought home to us the need for water breaks during the working day and we would remind each other to stop from time to time for a drink break. As well as gallons of water, we went through about fifteen cans of Coca-Cola a day between us.

And so we continued to work through the body bags in the refrigerated container. On the second day, we completed a further four cases, though I had hoped to complete at least five or six. We had streamlined procedures to the point where we could conclude a case in two to three hours, including writing up the report and cleaning the instruments. The patterns of injury we found during the examinations unerringly corroborated the testimony of the survivors. Sharp force trauma in the form of hacking with a machete and stabbing with a conventional knife was the most common cause of death, as was the effect of blunt force trauma from beating with clubs and rifle butts. Some victims had died as a result of the combination of both stabbing and beating; much more force than that needed to cause death had been inflicted on these victims. Often an individual injury would not have been enough to cause death on its own. In these cases, the cause of death was multiple injuries.

Again and again we saw similar patterns of trauma that indicated a frenzied machete attack. The single most common specific pattern of sharp force trauma was to the side of the neck and back of the head, probably denoting decapitation or attempted decapitation. The finding of a single fine line on the bones in the throat area was indicative of the throat being cut rather than of beheading. Frequently, too, there were machete wounds to the right or left shoulder in addition to trauma to the rib cage. The injury patterns were so similar on some bodies that I thought it was possible that one person could have been responsible for all of them.

Some forearm bones showed evidence of machete wounds, some delivered with such force that they had severed the bone right through. These injuries indicated defence trauma as the victims held up their arms in a futile effort to protect themselves. Gunshot injury was uncommon, but where present was immediately obvious. Several cases showed the distinctive entry and occasional exit pattern of a bullet fired at close range, often in the back of the head. This indicated that the deceased had been murdered in an assassination style, probably kneeling down with their hands tied behind them while they were shot in the back of the head. Gunshot deaths were rare, though. Most of the young men had been systematically hacked and bashed to death.

The horrifying findings continued. I had difficulty identifying the cause of death with one partially skeletonised body and the examination took almost three hours. This was a particularly unpleasant case to handle, as there was a considerable amount of decomposed soft tissue adhering to the bones. I could see no signs of injury immediately apparent in the remaining tissue. Upon closer examination, I eventually found a slender incised injury on the bone at the front of the neck. This injury, probably caused by a long-bladed knife, extended onto the left collarbone and was consistent with a knife gliding across the collarbone and neck. There was also a subtle transverse-oriented cut to the clothing. I ultimately concluded that this complex of injuries was evidence that this man had had his throat cut from behind by the assailant. The victim had his hands bound at the time.

Towards the end of that day, as we were tidying up, the civilian police arrived with the first of what I came to call the 'While you are here, Doc' cases. The police had come to ask whether I would be prepared to examine an alleged rapist being held at the prison compound. I was a bit taken aback and felt obliged to explain that my expertise lay in forensic pathology rather than in the examination of living victims or suspects. But then, I had been a full-time GP for eight years, so I was certainly able to examine a man apprehended for an offence like this. They took me along to the prison compound where a local East Timorese man had been charged. The alleged offence was that of rape of a western woman. I performed a clinical examination and found that the man had a case of florid gonorrhoea. It was crucial to convey this immediately to the victim and the victim's doctor so that the victim could be treated straight away. I wrote up a report, which confirmed some physical characteristics of the suspect as described by the victim, and handed it to the police on the spot. I later heard that the suspect had managed to escape from the jail, but was recaptured shortly afterwards. Although I was told that I might be required to present evidence at his trial, this did not happen. I heard on a later mission that he had been successfully prosecuted.

At the end of that day, it was finally confirmed that the murder trial in Melbourne was due to begin on 28 February. As I had feared, this meant that I would have to be home one week earlier than scheduled. It was possible that I could return to East Timor to complete the mission if there were bodies yet to be examined in the refrigerator. The following morning I told Matt and Shayne the news and we all resolved to complete the remaining cases in the eight days we had left. This obviously required starting earlier and working later, but all were happy to do this. I was grateful for their dedication and their enthusiasm.

We quickly settled into a routine, generally beginning at six o'clock each day and finishing around eight o'clock in the evening. We enjoyed working together, which greatly helped getting through the caseload. We also enjoyed the company of the soldiers in the room next door. This happy gang seemed to be genuinely pleased to be part of the INTERFET mission. In addition to acting as our security guards, they were more than happy to help out whenever we needed an extra hand to carry a body bag in from the refrigerator. We'd share the odd cigarette and can of Coke with them when we had a breather. For lunch we would quickly grab a packet of noodles and cup of black coffee in between cases. One day Shayne produced a block of army chocolate, which is not much more than compressed chocolate powder. I could not have enjoyed it more if it had been the finest Belgian chocolate.

The word 'mank' is one of those made-up words, taken up by the team and the soldiers. It describes the offensive substance produced by the combination of decomposed tissue and mud. The soldiers stuck up a 'Mank Free Zone' sign on the front door of their office to discourage us from walking in there with our contaminated gumboots. The smell of decomposed tissue is pervasive, but as we were working in such an environment continuously, we got so used to it that we didn't even notice it. But when I mixed with people at the UN compound, or at the house in Lhani, people pointed out that I stank. Even a shower at the end of the day did little to reduce the smell, which seemed to penetrate the skin.

I felt lethargic in the evenings, the combination of a long and demanding work day and the heat and humidity. At the end of each day, I would return to the small house at Lhani. Although the days were long and tiring, after-hours was something of a lonely period for me. I would have a simple dinner of spicy rice and fish with fruit for dessert. The tropical fruit, particularly the small bananas, looked fairly unpromising, but tasted delicious. After my evening meal, I would generally sit on the veranda and have a beer and read a novel, and just take in the surroundings of the evening. The temperature was high and the humidity was overbearing, but it was pleasant to sit back and listen to the chirps of the geckos and the racket caused by the cicadas in the nearby trees surrounding the compound. At exactly eight o'clock every night, the geckos would start chirping in a very distinctive way that I have not heard elsewhere. The locals call these 'fuck you' geckos, because that is exactly what their chirps sound like. I missed my family back at home and tried to call them, but couldn't get through on my mobile phone. It would occasionally work but would more often than not drop out. There are only one or two places in Dili where you could be guaranteed communication. One was a small hut the size of a telephone box on the way to Liquica, but I never had much luck getting through at the house.

Sidney would usually get home quite late, often after midnight, and several of the other UN members also worked irregular hours. I would occasionally have dinner with Sidney and some of her work colleagues if they were home, and share a Scotch together if time permitted. Because we all worked long hours, we went to bed quite early, usually around nine or ten o'clock, after a bit of a chat about the day's activities. I was very impressed by Sidney's ability to work to all hours. In addition to her work at the UN compound, she was very involved in public relations. She managed to fit in radio and television interviews at all hours and she spent a lot of time on the phone to international journalists. She seemed to be tireless. She had often left the house by the time I got up for work and came home quite late after dealing with matters relating to her human rights activities.

On the Sunday, we decided to ease up a little and Shayne took me for an afternoon drive along the north coast through beautiful villages to a long curved beach. There is a large statue of Christ on a hill at the end of the beach. It was presented to the people of East Timor by the Indonesians and for this reason is not particularly revered. We went for a steep walk up the hill to the statue. I had thought it would be pleasant to see some of the countryside that had not been destroyed, but even here there was evidence of the violence the country had suffered. Concrete shelters shaped like shells were dotted along the beach. Although there could have been absolutely no reason to do so, many of these shelters built for visitors to the beach had been smashed and destroyed.

In the early hours of one morning, I was awoken by a sharp bite on my leg. My first thought was that it was a mosquito carrying malaria or dengue and that death was imminent. I swatted my leg and felt another bite on my chest, and then another on the side of my neck. I jumped up to turn on the light and was relieved to find that I was covered in bull-ants rather than mosquitoes. They must have been after the packet of barley sugar I had in my bag. I was thankful for the can of flyspray I had packed and sprayed a perimeter around my mattress and in the crack in the wall they had come from. This did the job and I managed to fall back to sleep enveloped in a haze of humid air and insecticide.

I was very conscious of the time constraints and kept a close watch on our progress. We were able to get through some of the cases quite rapidly. One bag contained only a skull with a well-defined bullet entry wound. The cause of death in this case was not a matter of dispute. Others contained just a few bones. One bag contained the mixed remains of at least two individuals. This was because the bones had been scattered in the low-lying grass and bushes around the gravesites. Many of these remains revealed distinct gnawing marks, confirming that animals were responsible for the scattering of the bones. Sadly, in a few cases there was insufficient skeletal material to comment on gender, height or a cause of death. Bags with these types of minimal contents were like catch-up cases. We were definitely getting through the job. We were almost halfway through the fifty-one cases we had to examine, and all seemed to be going quite well.

Towards the end of one typical working day, a team of Czechoslovakian photojournalists arrived. The work of the UN in East Timor was attracting international attention. The journalists had requested access to the mortuary to document the killings in East Timor and the autopsy process in particular. I spent about thirty minutes with them describing the autopsy process and showing examples of typical injuries. The story was due to be screened in Prague soon and I asked for a copy of the video to be sent to my address in Australia. I am still waiting.

On day seven, I had gastroenteritis again, in spite of stopping taking the anti-malarials and being diligent with hand-washing and drinking only bottled water. I also developed severe lower-back pain from kneeling on the tiled floor while doing the initial examination of the bodies. I was forced to lie down for a while and when I felt better I passed dark urine the colour of Coca-Cola. I wondered whether I had in fact passed a small kidney stone and doubled my fluid intake to prevent any possibility of renal failure. The incidence of kidney stones in tropical climates is high because of the combination of borderline dehydration and spicy food. Despite my illness, I still felt strongly motivated to get our work done. We managed to complete a further five examinations on this day, as all of the bodies were fully skeletonised, with minimal dirt, decomposed tissue or clothing to remove. All of these were young men between the ages of eighteen and twenty-five years.

We continued to work through the long days at a good rate. Despite the heat and humidity, and although I hadn't eaten any food for a couple of days, I still didn't feel hungry or nauseated and my energy levels still seemed high.

One day, after waiting around for the water supply to be reconnected, we opened one of the two body bags that had been set aside that were not related to the Passabe massacre. The contents are something that I will never forget. It contained the bodies of a mother and her five children who had all been killed in Atabe. I was surprised that the bag weighed only a few kilograms. When I opened it, I could see very few bones. Several rugs and small items of clothing were mixed with skull fragments and the occasional long bone. It took some time to separate the bone fragments from the clothing. We then reconstructed the skull fragments using adhesive tape. Once we'd finished, we placed the skull fragments one against the other in order of descending size. What we were clearly looking at was the skulls of the mother and her five children of descending age. The smallest skull was that of a toddler. There were no apparent injuries on these bones, and I was fearful that we would not have enough remains to establish a cause of death.

After we had reconstructed the skulls though, a suspicious pattern of fracture at the back of the skull became evident. It appeared that the militia in this case had not even wasted bullets on this mother with her children. They had almost certainly bludgeoned them to death with heavy, blunt instruments. The little pairs of thongs and a small baby's jumpsuit in the body bag brought the horror of this atrocity home and we all stood back in silence. The brutality of this scenario escaped no one. Now, when I show photographs of the East Timor mission to colleagues, I am always choked up when I get to the point of describing this case. I recall clearly my visceral feelings of disgust and horror as the little skulls were being reassembled.

The other non-Passabe case that had been set aside for examination involved a thirty-year-old man from Liquica. All cases of this nature are tragic, but some I remember more than others. The story relayed to me by the investigators was that the militia had come up to this man at the front of his house and asked him in a fairly non-confrontational and friendly way what he felt about independence. It is alleged that when the man responded by saying that it seemed like a good idea to him, he was shot with a semi-automatic rifle approximately thirty times in full view of his wife and children.

From a cold forensic point of view, I felt that this case would be easy to conclude. Most of the bullets would surely have passed through the body, but fragments of bullet jacketing and possibly projectiles should still be present in some areas. The first stage of examination was to examine the body and clothing. We had difficulty removing the clothing, but when we had finally managed it, we could not see any bullet holes. I was then told that the wife had changed the bloodied clothing and redressed the body before burial.

The body was not completely skeletonised. There was a considerable amount of decomposed tissue remaining. As I worked, I saw small fragments of bluish green crumbling material in several areas of the soft tissues of the body. This was evidence of gunshot injury. The copper jacketing of bullets often separates on impact, and when combined with the acidity and water content of the body during decomposition turns into readily recognisable blue-green, crumbly, oxidised fragments. The upper-right chest area, although grossly decomposed, showed at least five rounded defects, which were in keeping with a cluster of bullets hitting the chest from an automatic weapon. While this was evidence in itself, a bullet would provide incontrovertible proof. An x-ray machine would have been invaluable in this case. Routine radiological examination of a decomposed body can still demonstrate the telltale evidence of fine lead fragments and occasionally the intact projectile core or jacket. During the autopsy, only one rib showed evidence of fragmentation. The remainder of the skeleton was intact. While I was examining the remains of the internal organs, I felt something firm in between my fingers. I was delighted to extract an intact 7.62 calibre fully jacketed projectile from the pelvic tissues. This one single item would be of enormous evidential significance should the case come to trial. Examining the rifling marks of the projectile under a microscope could prove a connection between it and any gun implicated in the shooting. Finding such concrete evidence made this a very satisfying case.

We carried on at a rapid pace. The majority of cases were literally more of the same: machete chops to the skull, back of the neck and torso, and evidence of torture. By the end of day ten, we were confident that the mission could be completed in the time allowed. Only twelve cases remained.

Although the monsoon season had begun, heavy downfalls

were rare and we could find no relief from the oppressive heat. One afternoon, the sound of rain crashing on the roof was deafening. We went outside and stood in rain for ten minutes or so to cool off. The sensation of warm rain over our foul-smelling scrubsuits was wonderful. They dried off within minutes of re-entering the air-conditioned mortuary.

A few cases stood out from the others. With only three days left to go, we were surprised to find identification on one of the bodies. This was rare. In all previous cases, the bodies had been robbed of personal possessions. The identification card included the name, address and date of birth of the deceased. Why it was there was puzzling. Perhaps the militia had missed it. We put it aside as evidence. Another case examined on this day revealed one victim's skull had been cut into small fragments by a machete. Reassembly of the skull fragments disclosed five independent and intersecting sharp cuts across the skull causing a jigsaw-like fragmentation. Although I was dealing with atrocities all day every day, occasionally I would shake my head in bewilderment at what I was seeing. One or two of those blows would have killed this individual.

I wanted to examine the weapons that caused these injuries. Forensically, it is interesting to correlate the injuries with a typical machete. Shayne told me that machetes were available at the local market for twenty Australian dollars. He then suggested that I take one or two of them home to show my fellow pathologists the implements used in these atrocities. He gave me two machetes from the many thousands that had been confiscated from the militia after the intervention of INTERFET. I declared that these machetes constituted items of evidence at customs and immigration on my return and they were duly allowed through into Australia.

We were now only two days away from completing the mission and morale was high, although we were all conscious of the fact that the last day would be a difficult one. We examined a further eight body bags. Unfortunately, several of the bags contained only a few bones, which made findings regarding the cause of death impossible, though they were very quickly processed in fifteen to twenty minutes. One of these bags only contained a couple of ribs and a t-shirt. Incredibly, this victim was later identified by the distinctive pattern on the t-shirt.

Now it was time to examine the body bag that Matt had strongly suggested we do last. Matt's advice was good. The last body bag in the refrigerator weighed considerably more than any of the others. It took three people to carry it from the refrigerated container to the mortuary. I was told that this was a nineteen-year-old man who was killed at Passabe. His body was more or less intact, although profoundly decomposed. When I opened the body bag I saw that the skin was essentially intact, although extensively discoloured and in some places mummified. All clothing items remained on the body. We searched his pockets and found a wallet containing approximately twenty thousand rupiah and an identification card stating his name, date and place of birth and religion. There was also a watch. It was hard to imagine how these items had been missed by the militia, but at least we had a second victim with firm identification.

We began by removing the clothing. We could not see any form of defect that would have been in keeping with stabbing or shooting. The skin, although grossly decomposed and discoloured, did not show any significant incised defects that would go with cutting and slashing from a machete. I was baffled. We decided that the only way to establish the cause of death was to entirely skeletonise the body. This is a procedure that is not performed commonly at home and it was time-consuming and unpleasant in the extreme. I could identify no injuries on the major bones of the skeleton after de-fleshing the body. In an ironic twist, it was beginning to look as though I would not find the cause of death in this case, even though we had the entire body. But the decision to de-flesh the body was well worth the effort. After a lengthy close examination, I identified a single incised defect to the spine on the front of the neck. Despite the lack of external evidence, we had managed to confirm that this man had had his throat cut. Worse still, while the body was still fleshed, we had observed evidence of amputation of the genitalia. I was informed that it was common for various forms of torture to be inflicted on victims—cutting off of hands, feet and genitals was relatively commonplace.

## MISSION COMPLETED

It was the last working day. We managed to deal with the nine remaining body bags quite quickly as they represented the remains of at least four individuals. Many of the bags contained several bones, most of which did not bear signs of injury, so we were unable to establish the probable cause of death. We couldn't assess gender or height either because the remaining bones didn't provide enough information. In all, the forty-nine body bags from Passabe contained the remains of at least forty-eight bodies. All of the bodies were placed back in the refrigerated container to await identification and, finally, to be returned home to their villages and families.

We now had to meticulously clean the mortuary for the team that would follow us. With mops, scrubbing brushes, buckets and copious amounts of soap and water, we started cleaning. After ten days of overwork, borderline dehydration and constant exposure to horror, we dutifully cleaned the room. And then, in an outburst of hilarity and relief, the large, white, highly polished tiled floor became a skating rink. We skated around the floor in our gumboots, occasionally slipping over on the wet floor to great shouts of laughter.

After changing into a clean pair of scrubs, it was time for the obligatory team shot. I am a great sentimentalist. My office at work is lined with many team shots from missions in East Timor, Kosova and the Solomon Islands. In this case, there was only the three of us. As our work was just about over, we talked one of the civilian police into taking several photographs, one of which now hangs above my desk in my office.

Then gallows humour took over in the relief at having finished the job. I ducked back into the storeroom and put on my purple jocks on the outside of my scrubsuit. Shayne drew a large capital M on the front of my scrubs and then he produced a 9 millimetre holstered Glock pistol, which I placed around my waist. With hands on hips, we were photographed again. So 'Mank Man' was born (me) and 'Bone Boy' (Matt). We were super heroes—at least in our own minds.

## GOING HOME

On the final day (day thirteen), we took several hours to collate the reports and do a final tidy up of the facility. Matt photocopied all the reports and I submitted the original signed copies to the SCIU. These were to be passed to the prosecution team as documentary evidence of the cold-blooded murder of the victims. I took the copies home with me to store in my office. Although I was eager to get back home, I was now rather sad to say goodbye to the rest of the team, in particular Sidney Jones. The night before my departure, we went to a Portuguese restaurant as a last supper. After saying our goodbyes, I returned back to the house at Lhani for my last sleep in East Timor and flew out the following morning. Sidney was sad to see me go and had commented that the effort of the team was nothing short of fantastic.

The trip back on the Hercules to Darwin was not as rough as the one going over. As I left the airport at Dili, I noticed that the UN flag was at half-mast. I asked one of the civilian police why, and he told me that one of the police officers had died of dengue fever the night before.

The plane touched down at the RAAF base in Darwin. The cyclone fence surrounding customs and immigration surprised me. Soldiers with guard dogs were patrolling. It felt like we were the bad guys. One officer had a pair of forceps and he conscientiously picked out all mud, grass and seeds from the tread of my boots. If I'd known that this would happen, I'd have cleaned the boots more thoroughly before I got there. The customs officials meticulously examined everyone's luggage regardless of whether or not anything had been declared. They pulled out all my dirty washing from their plastic bags and examined the internal zippered compartments of all suitcases and bags. I was left to repack my gear, which was not easy. I needed help to zip up the suitcase before I could get on the bus to take me back to the hotel. The two machetes, which had been flagged as evidential items, passed through without comment.

Back at the hotel, I luxuriated in my first hot shower in several weeks. After a hamburger and bottle of white wine, I slept deeply. There was a definite anticlimax when I got home; I found it difficult to readjust to my mundane daily routine. Having survived the ordeal of third-world forensic pathology and having succeeded in examining fifty-one cases in ten working days, I felt

Little remained of the city of Dili after the wanton destruction brought about by the Indonesian backed militia. February 2000.

The graffiti on the wall of this building speaks volumes of the grief and anguish of the innocent folk of East Timor. February 2000.

The refrigerated container houses fifty-one body bags awaiting post-mortem examination. The majority of these victims relate to the massacre at Passabe. February 2000.

The first forensic team to perform formal post-mortem examinations in East Timor, February 2000. L–R: Matthew Skinner, Malcolm Dodd and Shayne Towers-Hammond.

Most of the initial post-mortem inspections were performed on the floor of the temporary mortuary set up at the Agricultural College in Dili, February 2000. Almost all bodies were in an exceedingly poor condition and required a keen eye to identify important evidential material.

The exhumation site at Aituto, January 2001. Two bodies were buried in a deep ravine. The mother of one of the victims expresses her profound grief as the bodies are unearthed.

My meeting with President Xanana Gusmao in December 2002. The President wished to hear the results of my post-mortem examinations first-hand following the Dili shoot-out.

Mank man lives! Outside the mortuary, Dili, February 2000.

An aerial view of the city of Pristina taken from the UN helicopter as we flew into Serbian-held territory to undertake photography of potential exhumation sites. May 2000.

Exhumations at Dragadan cemetery on the outskirts of Pristina. Within hours, a mass grave was exposed. May 2000.

Here I am pictured with members of the British Forensic Team (BFT) during the process of exhumation at Dragadan cemetery, May 2000.

The beautiful city of Prizren (the ancient capital of Kosova) did not escape bomb damage during the conflict. May 2000.

A view of the walk through the 'bomb garden' at Pristina, May 2000. The invaluable instruction provided at this facility came a little too late for this forensic rotation.

An example of the live ordnance that may be encountered in the field. The possibility of booby-trapped bodies in mass graves was always in our minds.

The first contingent of the British forensic team, May 2000. This outing was marred by a tragic bomb blast fatality of an innocent child, a legacy of the unexploded ordnance that litters Kosova.

that I would easily be able to take on further overseas missions. No sooner had I got back home than I was eager to set off on the next mission. I wondered why more Australian forensic pathologists were not eager to do such work. It had given me an excellent opportunity to contribute to an international humanitarian effort; it had enhanced my forensic skills, particularly in the examination of skeletal remains; and I had formed firm friendships with overseas workers, particularly from INTERFET and the UN, many of whom I still correspond with.

During the ten days spent working in the mortuary, I took numerous photographs. These were not as evidence, but rather to document all the work that had been performed. They have proven to be an invaluable teaching aid for trainee pathologists. They are also a photo document of the mission that I show to pathologist colleagues and other special interest groups.

Unfortunately, the criminal investigations into the human rights violations in East Timor have resulted in few convictions. The SCIU and special panels established by the UN issued indictments against 391 people, including the former Indonesian Defence Minister, Wiranto. Indonesia's Ad Hoc Human Rights Court for Timor-Leste in Jakarta indicted eighteen military and police personnel, two government officials and a militia leader with attacks on civilians in the post-referendum period, but no high-ranking officers were charged. Of the eighteen who were tried, only one gang leader was convicted. Sadly, most of those responsible for the inhumane acts, forced deportations, persecution, torture and assassinations have not been called to justice, and there has been much frustration as the higher ranking militia members have escaped, with the lower ranks only being arrested and then often successfully appealing. A recent report by a UN Commission of Experts has criticised Indonesia's court process and has requested that the militia and security forces be prosecuted or retried for the pre-independence atrocities by an international tribunal.

The UN funded a Special Panel for Serious Crimes in East Timor. Three judges from the panel travelled to Passabe in 2004 to hear seven witnesses give testimony in the trial of a former militia-man on trial on eight counts of crimes against humanity, including his alleged participation in the Passabe massacre. Florenco Tacaqui is one of eleven accused persons charged in an indictment related to the Passabe massacre in September 2001. Approximately one hundred members of the community attended the trial from Passabe, demonstrating the level of community concern that those responsible be brought to justice. Although there have been indictments and convictions related to the Passabe massacre, I was not called upon to give evidence, so I assume that the reports we submitted were sufficient as documentary evidence.

The year 2000 was shaping up to be a busy time. Several months later I found myself in Kosova.

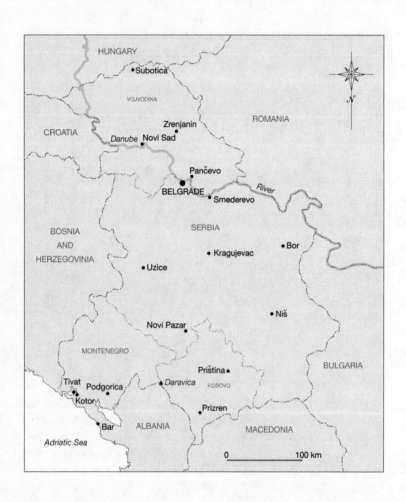

# THREE

# KOSOVA
## MAY 2000

## KOSOVA

The recent bitter ethnic conflict in the former Yugoslavia has a long and complex history. Islamic Albanians, who have lived in the country for centuries, constitute ninety per cent of the population of Kosova. Alongside the Albanians live a minority of Serbs, who are largely Serbian Orthodox. The events leading up to the war crimes investigated by international forensic teams began in 1989 when President Slobodan Milosevic reignited dormant hostilities by arranging the elimination of Kosova's autonomy. Federal Republic of Yugoslavia (FRY) forces and Serb paramilitary groups forced Kosovar Albanian workers out of their jobs and replaced them with Serbs. Schools and universities were closed and Albanians were denied the most basic of rights. This prompted the Kosovar Albanians to begin non-violent resistance to the rule of Belgrade, but in response to continued suppression and attacks from the Serbian police, the Kosova Liberation Army (KLA) began bombing and attacking Serbian police and state officials.

Despite the establishment of a parallel Kosovar government in 1990, which had declared independence from Serbia, negotiations failed and the conflict escalated. People who had until recently lived alongside each other for years now turned against one another as houses were burnt and people murdered. International pleas for the hostilities to cease were ignored and approximately ten thousand Kosovar Albanians died in ethnic cleansing atrocities. An estimated eight hundred thousand refugees were forced across the border from Kosova, their homes looted and destroyed. En route, many were killed, abused and robbed. After the hostilities had subsided, many thousands more were killed trying to re-enter Kosova in heavily mined border crossings. Up to five hundred thousand more Albanian Kosovars were displaced within Kosova.

Kosova has been under the authority of the UN Interim Administration Mission in Kosova (UNMIK) since June 1999. In February 2003, the Federal Republic of Yugoslavia Parliament ratified the Constitutional Charter, establishing a new state union and changing the name of the country from Yugoslavia to Serbia and Montenegro. Kosova is currently an international protectorate administered by the United Nations, while technically still a part of Serbia and Montenegro. The supreme legal authority in Kosova is UNMIK.

While I was working in East Timor, the ethnic cleansing occurring in Kosova caused the deaths of many thousands of people. Due to the enormity of the tragedy, the UN had requested international intervention to investigate the deaths and to gather the necessary evidence for charges to be laid against the perpetrators of war crimes and crimes against humanity. To this end, forensic experts had been enlisted from around the world to work on rotation as part of the ongoing UN effort. The evidence gathered and documented by the international forensic teams would be submitted to the UN International Criminal Tribunal for the Former Yugoslavia (ICTY) in The Hague. Other staff from the Victorian Institute of Forensic Medicine (VIFM) had already volunteered their services. Professor Stephen Cordner had done a rotation at Orahovac in Kosova in early 2000, where a vehicle testing station served as the mortuary. Dr Michael Burke, a fellow forensic pathologist from the VIFM, had done similar work in a grainstore in Xerxe in 1999. Associate Director Dr David Ranson did a stint in Pristina following my own.

A few weeks after my return from East Timor, I responded to the call from the United Kingdom requesting further volunteers to assist in the effort in Kosova. Many British and European pathologists had already spent time there and the pool of forensic specialists available was diminishing. So the call had gone out to Australia to put forward names of forensic pathologists willing to assist in the investigation of war crimes in the post-war period. Although the scale and nature of the atrocities committed in Kosova were different from those in East Timor, I thought that I had gained enough experience in the investigation of war crimes to be of assistance.

As in East Timor, the task of the forensic teams was to conduct autopsies on the bodies to establish cause of death of the victims, and to record information to assist with identification. As many victims in Kosova had been shot, we would have to retrieve all the evidential items that could be used in a court of law, such as bullets, projectiles and shrapnel, as well as items that could help in personal identification. As well as conducting the autopsy, we could also be required to help exhume bodies from mass gravesites. Although I hadn't done that before, I volunteered with little hesitation. Since my return from East Timor, I was eager to do similar work again. While my day-to-day work at the VIFM was very satisfying, I missed the challenges and demands I faced while working in East Timor and I wanted to work on a war crime investigation with a forensic team. I hoped it would enable me to hone my skills as a forensic pathologist still further.

About six weeks after my return from East Timor, a list of names that would ultimately comprise Team One was finalised and put forward. Team One would consist of me as forensic pathologist, and fourteen other dedicated professionals. This was an established system that had already been extremely efficient in the investigation of post-war atrocities. The prime moving force of Team One was the British Forensic Team (BFT) from Scotland Yard in London. The BFT was working in close alliance with the United Nations International Criminal Tribunal for the Former Yugoslavia (ICTY). This tribunal was created in 1993 to replace the existing UN Commission of Experts on the conflict in Yugoslavia. The ICTY organised its own forensic team and one of its areas of investigation, the one I was to participate in, was related to the crimes committed by Serbian forces against the Kosovar Albanian population during 1999 to 2000. Sixty scientists from many different countries participated in this investigation, during which the bodies of more than a thousand of the estimated ten thousand dead were exhumed and examined. In contrast to East Timor, I didn't need to spend any time wondering how I was going to complete the work alone and in unknown conditions.

I departed Melbourne on 11 May 2000 and travelled Qantas business class to London Heathrow. British and European pathologists flew economy class due to the shorter travel distances, but I was very pleased with the UN policy of flying forensic personnel business class over vast distances. The flight over was uneventful other than to say it was tantamount to staying at the Hilton at ten thousand metres—a world away from the people travelling in the rows behind me and light years away from the C-130 Hercules. After a restful flight, I easily passed through customs and immigration at Heathrow, gathered my luggage and caught a shuttle bus to Gatwick Airport. After a short wait in the transit lounge, I boarded a British Airways business class flight to Macedonia. To my great surprise, I was the only passenger in the business class section and therefore had three flight attendants at my beck and call. I could definitely get used to this!

## MACEDONIA TO KOSOVA

The traveller to Macedonia cannot get a visa from Australia before leaving, so on arriving at Skopje airport in Macedonia, I presented myself for the involved process of having my passport checked and visa issued. Two heavily armed and intimidating female officers took possession of my passport for scrutiny and I was ordered to sit in the arrival lounge to wait for the visa to be processed. As I sat under the threatening gaze of the armed immigration officials, I watched my luggage go around and around on the carousel. Fearing that it might be moved, I got up to retrieve it. The officials glared at me and motioned me to sit back in my seat at the point of a gun. I didn't argue, I got the message! This level of intimidation seemed unnecessary, given that the UN staff had no choice but to go through this process of visa allocation at Skopje. The officials seemed to enjoy the opportunity to flex their official muscles while they had the chance to do so. All other travellers to Kosova have a similar tale to tell. Thirty minutes later, the documentation was processed and I left the airport with my passport and visa. After this minor ordeal, I wondered what was in store for me next, but I was relieved to be met by a cheerful UN driver holding up a placard with my name on it. We loaded up the UN 4WD and he drove me to the capital city of Pristina.

The drive through the surrounding countryside in the afternoon sun was magnificent. The weather in May was beautifully warm and mild with the temperature in the mid to high twenties. Deep valleys and ravines were flanked on either side by steep snow-capped mountains. The trip from Skopje to Pristina took several hours and we were delayed by frequent halts at security checkpoints for passport and visa examinations. Such delays were very frustrating, but, like the airport experience, they just had to be accepted. We were not alone. Several kilometres of heavily laden trucks were backed up in service lanes waiting for similar document checks. Occasionally I saw large Leopard tanks with the distinctive KFOR painted on the side. KFOR stood for the Kosova force assigned to peacekeeping in the region. Closer to the city, I noticed several Serbian Orthodox churches with heavily sand-bagged perimeters, frequently surrounded by razor wire and large searchlights. The driver told me that the Serbian churches were still considered to be a potential target of attack by rebellious Albanian forces, so it was practical for the UN KFOR troops to use these churches as security checkpoints. In spite of the huge civil upheaval, the majority of houses in this area were in good order, many displaying neat front gardens and colourful floral window boxes.

We finally arrived in Pristina in the late evening. The city had had a population of approximately a quarter of a million people before the civil war. In the post-war period, many people had crossed the border to re-enter Kosova and the population had swelled to approximately a million. As a result, the town's centre was heavily polluted and the traffic was absolutely chaotic and constantly gridlocked. Many of the cars had no registration plates. We were told that these vehicles were stolen and had been smuggled across the borders by unlicensed drivers.

High-rise residential buildings dominate the city of Pristina, with conspicuous white satellite dishes in every window. I was surprised to see that virtually all of the buildings in Pristina remained intact, despite the civil war. This was in sharp contrast to the images on the news of Belgrade, where numerous sites of bombing by North Atlantic Treaty Organization (NATO) forces had occurred. In Pristina, only three targets were singled out by NATO forces for destruction. These targets included the Serb army barracks, a nearby fuel dump and the communications building in the centre of the city, which was an example of precision bombing. It was no more than a pile of rubble, but an intact high-rise building stood immediately beside it. The Serb barracks had been laid waste and across the road a fuel dump had been hit. The crumpled and partially collapsed fuel tanks stood out from a field of twisted metal and rubble. I was warned to avoid this site, as fragments of depleted uranium used on the tips of armour-piercing projectiles by the NATO forces were scattered about.

With the exception of these three sites and the public awareness signs placed about in the fields and forests warning of the dangers of various types of bombs, we saw little evidence of the recent bloodshed and violence. Occasionally a Leopard tank rumbled by and a few truckloads of heavily armed soldiers drove past, but these were really the only indications I could see of military intervention. The people of Pristina went about their daily lives and I was struck by the fashionable clothing worn by the young adults that would have been entirely in place in Paris or London.

I made a short visit to the UN headquarters and then we made our way through narrow, winding streets to the outer suburbs of Pristina, where my accommodation was located. Many of the houses in Kosova are two- to three-storey red-brick constructions. A family would build successive stories as they made the money to do so. As each level was completed, the family would move upward to occupy another floor. As a consequence, many of the houses were multileveled and in various stages of completion.

After about twenty minutes, we arrived at a four-storey red-brick house, which was to be my accommodation for the following three weeks. This house had an interesting history. It had originally belonged to a Serb who had been run out of town. It was then promptly occupied by an Albanian squatter who was now charging the UN and the BFT rental. Dr Peter Ellis, the Director of Forensic Pathology at Westmead Hospital in Sydney, met me at the front door. Peter had just finished his three-week rotation with the BFT and was due to leave the following day. There had been few exhumations and autopsies during his rotation and he was very frustrated, given the long distance he had travelled and the amount of time he had spent without results. He was to return later in the year for a more productive tour, fortunately. His rotation would contrast sharply with what I was to experience in the following three weeks.

The team was an interesting mix of personalities. Ron Turnbull was the team leader and I was the forensic pathologist. The two forensic anthropologists from the Netherlands completed their tour shortly after I arrived and were replaced by Julie Roberts and John Rob. Steve Donlon was our colourful mortuary technician from Glasgow and Paul Scott, who preferred to be known as 'Scotty', was a radiographer from Yorkshire. The remainder of the team consisted of scene-of-crime officers, photographers, liaison officers, data processors and those who worked digging, exhuming and retrieving bodies. It was clear from the initial introductions that we would all get along extremely well and make an effective team; happily this proved to be the case in the weeks ahead.

## SETTLING IN

As I was shown to my room, I was pleasantly surprised by the contrast to the rudimentary lodgings in East Timor. The house had many bedrooms, several small kitchens and a communal television room on the top floor, which led to a beautiful rooftop garden.

This area was ideal for the team to come together at the end of the working day for a meal, chat and debrief. I was assigned a bedroom containing a very comfortable bed, a wardrobe and a desk. A modern bathroom was located immediately across the hallway from my bedroom. This shared living arrangement would contribute to the atmosphere of cooperation that existed among the team members. The thought of the good company at the end of the day would help me through the following few weeks. Although the team had a compulsory debrief by psychiatrists at the end of the mission, I found this quite unnecessary, and I think this was largely due to the camaraderie I experienced in the shared house.

In addition to the professional and experienced team and the comfortable lodgings, I also understood that the morgue was well established and fully functional. From what the team members said, I could expect the best of all possible situations. I anticipated that this would mean that there would be much less pressure on me to do anything other than perform autopsies on the exhumed bodies in an attempt to identify the victim and arrive at a reasonable cause of death. As in East Timor, this would involve a very thorough forensic examination of each body, beginning with meticulous external and internal examinations. But I would not be responsible for peripheral duties like documenting personal items and photography. Although the team in East Timor had been fantastic and we had successfully completed the mission, it was hampered by the lack of forensically trained technicians. I was very relieved at not having this worry and being able to focus on my assigned tasks.

The post-mortem facility set aside for our use was located at the forensic pathology department at the University of Pristina. Before I could begin, I was informed that the x-ray equipment at the mortuary had failed and that we would have to wait for an electrical engineer from Britain to arrive to replace a vital circuit board. The equipment was probably going to be out of action for three days. Rather than be idle, I volunteered to be part of the exhumation team. The exhumations were due to begin the next day and my expertise in body recovery was welcomed, limited though it was. I had not been part of a large-scale exhumation before and I found the prospect a little daunting, but I felt that I'd be able to contribute something to the team effort. The experience I gained would prove to be invaluable in later missions to East Timor and the Solomon Islands.

Early the next morning, the team got ready and we set off for Pristina for the UN induction process. We would then make an inspection of possible mass gravesites. We drove back along the winding narrow streets and past the rows of red-brick houses, with their distinctive terracotta tiled rooves. Thankfully, the induction process in Kosova was far less complicated than it was in East Timor. The entire process took no longer than an hour. All I had to do was to fill out a few brief forms, have a pass photograph taken and collect enough Deutschmarks to provide for my accommodation and food. Then the team assembled for an inspection of areas that had been identified as possible gravesites.

## SEARCHING FOR GRAVESITES

Our destination was a nearby Serbian church where there were thought to be several clandestine burial sites. During the ethnic cleansing of Kosova, in addition to summary executions, whole villages had been rounded up and shot by the Serbian troops. Others had been abducted and many thousands had fled their burnt and looted villages in terror. As the situation slowly returned to normal and people gradually returned to their homes, they observed many areas of disturbed soil that smelt foul. They would notify the authorities of these suspected burial sites, which were then noted for examination by the forensic teams.

We spent the afternoon at the church searching the areas that had been designated as suspicious. Norwegian infantry engineers, who worked with a team of cadaver and bomb detection dogs, helped us. Their highly trained black labradors were able to detect the smell associated with underground decomposition or explosives. It was fascinating to observe the techniques they used. The soldiers would pierce the ground with a stout wire and then remove it from the ground and slide it through a small red rubber ball. The rubber ball was then presented to the dog to sniff. If the dog immediately sat, it was a positive sign that there was a body buried beneath the ground. I was amazed at the dogs' abilities and dismayed to hear that they were shot after their working careers were over. This was because they were not able to live a normal life upon retirement, as their working lives were so demanding and stressful.

The perpetrators of the massacres were cunning and went to great lengths to hide evidence of the mass murders and to mislead investigators. We were told of exhumations being conducted on what turned out to be decoy gravesites. The digging would reveal only the body of a slain goat wrapped in a blanket. In addition to decoy and elaborately concealed graves, it was rumoured that there were booby-trapped graves, where bodies had been buried with live grenades attached. Another method of deception was to truck the victims' bodies—often Serbs would kill a whole village of Albanians—to different regions to avoid detection and make identification difficult. Presumably, these tactics were intended to frustrate investigators in the hope that they would give up and leave. But this didn't happen, and thorough, dedicated efforts to locate the victims of the ethnic cleansing were ongoing.

Unfortunately, all areas we examined that day failed to reveal evidence of human or animal remains.

Another ploy used by the Serbs to deceive investigators was to mix the graves of war crime victims together with conventional graves within the urban area in an attempt to conceal them. After our fruitless search at the Serbian church, our attention turned next to a legitimate Albanian cemetery at Dragadan. Intelligence sources had indicated that Serbian troops had disposed of large numbers of bodies in this otherwise legitimate burial ground. According to local intelligence, these graves were dug by the Serbian troops to bury the local Albanian villagers they had rounded up and shot in a brutal attack. Dragadan cemetery was about thirty minutes' drive from our base on the outskirts of Pristina. We drove along the now familiar maze of winding roads and cramped red-brick houses. We passed the occasional open marketplace and conspicuous ancient mosques with tall minarets that resembled rockets. The irony of this did not escape me.

The cemetery was located on the edge of a rolling hill overlooking a power station with large chimneys that belched out enormous quantities of acrid white-grey smoke. This smoke layered the plains under the influence of heavy, cold air. We got out and started to explore the site, which was littered with conventional gravestones and scattered numbered location sticks indicating the sites of recent burials awaiting grave markers. There were many well-established graves with large black rectangular slabs on which photographs of the dead were displayed. In between these established graves, we saw several very conspicuous tracts of disturbed soil, some measuring approximately twenty metres in length. It was clear that this large area of disturbed soil was not the result of the work of a few people armed with picks and shovels. It was obviously the well-orchestrated effort of troops using earth-moving equipment to dig large trenches for the express purpose of body disposal. Residents nearby had noted the coming and going of large earth-moving equipment in the dead of night.

## EXHUMATIONS

The site was suspicious enough to warrant further investigation and the forensic team got ready to dig for bodies. As a general precaution against contagion and contamination, we put on disposable white 'bunny' suits, gumboots and heavy gloves taped at the wrist. Heavily armed soldiers cordoned off and secured the perimeter. As with a crime scene back at home, all team members were logged in before entering. We made our way to the gravesite, where the Norwegian engineers had already arrived with large earth-moving machines. A bulldozer roared into life and began removing the raised soil and adjacent grass area over the suspected mass gravesite. All eyes were trained on the newly exposed soil for the first signs of a body or clothing. The engineer worked the huge machine with almost surgical precision. He was able to remove soil at twenty millimetre increments, ceasing only when the telltale signs of grey-brown decomposed tissue or clothing was exposed.

The anthropologists and I keenly watched each area of newly exposed soil for the first sign of a victim, which was the acrid smell of decomposition followed by the characteristic grey discolouration of soil surrounding decomposed flesh. After about twenty minutes, the shout went up to stop as a small fragment of fragile grey tissue came into view about one metre below the surface. The anthropologists and I jumped into the pit to examine the first fragment of grey material and to confirm the presence of a body beneath the soil. I used a garden trowel to tease away some of the immediate overlying soil and identified the sole of a foot.

Now that a body had been located, the rest of the exhumation team jumped in with shovels and trowels to define the margins of the body. We painstakingly removed the soil from around the body, gradually exposing a limb and a shard of torn clothing. As we removed each layer of soil we revealed further body parts and remnants of clothing. We took photographs and noted the depth of the remains from the surface. After a few hours, the full extent of what we could expect became evident. The initial small fragment of grey tissue led to the exposure of a body lying face down. The team carefully removed the body, revealing further victims lying immediately beneath it. As the day unfolded, I was confronted by the most grisly sight imaginable. The pit contained in excess of sixty bodies, all thrown in on top of each other and lying tangled together up to four deep.

We worked through the morning. The temperature continued to climb until it had reached the high twenties by midday. We sweated excessively in the bunny suits and had to stop every twenty or thirty minutes for a water break to prevent dehydration. We took our water and lunch breaks beside our vehicles and under tarpaulin tents erected for shade. The smell of the decomposing bodies was overwhelming. Many of the exhumation team chose to wear full-face respirators or at the very least, surgical masks. We managed to eat our lunch while avoiding the scene before our eyes as best we could.

As we worked on through the warm afternoon, locating further bodies along the tract of exposed soil, we inadvertently unearthed part of a legitimate Albanian burial. A wooden plank was placed at a forty-five degree angle at one end of the large open grave pit. Immediately beneath the plank was the decomposing body of an elderly female in a white shroud. Because the Serbs had used large earth-moving equipment to open the soil to dump the bodies, they had obscured some legitimate marking points for conventional burials. We decided that if we came across any further wooden boards, known locally as a *drraza*, we would not disturb the grave and body. We attempted to cause as little disruption as possible. It felt uncomfortable to be digging in an established cemetery, but we had no alternative if we were to locate the murder victims also buried there.

Most of the bodies had been dumped in the central part of the exposed pit and separating the entangled bodies was difficult. Once the soil was removed and the body mass revealed, the scene reminded me of the pictures I had seen of the mass graves found at Bergen-Belsen concentration camp at the end of the Second World War. The scene was surreal in its horror. We had to push feelings of revulsion aside so that we could work on to uncover the next victim.

Unfortunately, the gravesite was located on a naturally occurring water table. As we dug deeper, acrid brown water seeped into the grave, delaying the work. Exhumation team members bailed the water from the pit with buckets so work could continue. As we cleared the pit of mud and earth, we could see that all of the exposed bodies were in a state of advanced decomposition. It was difficult to gauge the amount of time the bodies had been buried. Local intelligence suggested that it might have been as long as six months. Although it was difficult to know the ages of these victims at first glance, the impression was that the majority were male Kosovar Albanians of military age and it seemed probable that they were the victims of a mass shooting.

In contrast to East Timor, where the majority of victims examined wore only a t-shirt or a pair of shorts, most of these bodies were heavily clothed, although a few were naked. As time went on, we would find that the graves we uncovered at the site in fact contained a mixture of bodies with different injuries, at different stages of decomposition, some clothed and some unclothed. We concluded that they were not all the result of a single massacre, but that some had probably died at different times and under different conditions. The couple of bodies we came across of the elderly and children were possibly legitimate burials, or they could have been related to this massacre. It was impossible to tell the exact circumstances under which all these people had ended up packed into the grave.

As we removed each body from the pit, it was photographed, placed in a body bag and given a number. As the day wore on, the body bags began to pile up against the mass grave awaiting their transfer to the mortuary facility in Pristina. The next few weeks at the mortuary were going to be busy. The total body count was likely to be above what I could examine in the two or so weeks remaining. I wasn't as concerned about this as I had been in East Timor facing a similar situation, though, because in Kosova any bodies I was unable to examine would be dealt with by the next pathologist on rotation.

By the end of the first day, we had recovered sixteen bodies. At night, members of the Royal Fusiliers, fondly referred to as 'budgies' after their distinctive feather-adorned caps, secured the exhumation site. The smell of the open graves drew scavenging animals and on a few occasions the Fusiliers were forced to shoot marauding dogs. They also mistakenly shot a cat. Although the soldiers were sanctioned to shoot dogs, there was no existing UN policy on cats and there was some light-hearted discussion the next morning about whether this action would be viewed as justifiable.

## THE MORTUARY

The following day, the team exhumed a further twenty-eight victims from the pit and each day would see more and more bodies retrieved. The bagged victims were loaded onto a dedicated army truck, which lumbered its way through the city streets of Pristina to the mortuary at the university. The University of Pristina is an impressive building next to the national hospital. The building houses the hospital's pathology laboratories and post-mortem facilities.

During the time of the conflict, the Albanian hospital personnel were expelled by the invading Serb armies and replaced by their own staff. I heard horrifying accounts of Albanian patients allegedly being forcibly removed from their hospital beds to accommodate incoming Serb casualties. Stories abounded of bedridden patients being either shot or removed to make hospital beds available. Such atrocities defied belief and I wondered whether any of the victims in the grave we had exhumed had suffered this terrible fate.

The body storage facility was reached by a basement ramp leading from the main carpark of the hospital. Shovels and picks for digging, body bags and large paper bags used for evidential material such as clothes were stored in metal containers near the entry to the morgue. The basement facility was rudimentary at best and it had a rather sinister atmosphere. It was littered with open coffins and several discarded post-mortem tables. There was a large incinerator standing in one corner. The shiny new refrigerated body containers supplied by the UN would become filled to capacity almost immediately.

The post-mortem room was on the third floor, linked to the basement by an elevator. I optimistically assumed this would provide an efficient system for transporting several body bags on a trolley to the post-mortem room. Unfortunately, the elevator broke down frequently and when this happened we had to carry the body bags up the stairwell of the hospital. This was in full view of hospital staff and visitors. It would have been a very unpleasant experience for people visiting their sick relatives to see us lugging body bags up the hospital stairwell, reeking of the unmistakable and overpowering stench of decomposition.

The post-mortem facility, on the other hand, was much better than I had expected. There were two well-equipped autopsy rooms, one for routine hospital cases and the other for the forensic work of the BFT. .This was a large, well-lit room, containing two modern post-mortem tables, each with a source of running water. The full and comprehensive set of post-mortem instruments were sharp and in good condition. In contrast to the spartan post-mortem facility at Dili, everything we could possibly need was supplied. There was adequate ventilation and room for post-mortem technicians, photographers, anthropologists and scene-of-crime officers. Steve, our forensic technician, proved to be an exceptionally competent mortuary technician, as well as having a wicked sense of humour, which was welcomed during the gruelling examination process.

Although the facilities differed greatly from East Timor, as did the types of injury inflicted on the victims, our purpose was the same—to attest to the cause and manner of death and begin the process of identification. The forensic examination required meticulous scrutiny of the body, including accompanying clothing and personal items. We were to document all injuries in a UN pro-forma and set aside projectiles and fragments of shrapnel as evidential material. In all respects, the post-mortem examination employed by the BFT adhered to universal guidelines that had been employed in East Timor and would be used in my later missions to the Solomon Islands. I selected a large area of bench space adjacent to one of the windows to set up the post-mortem pro-formas and personal camera equipment, and was ready to begin.

We were to find that the vast majority of victims had been shot dead or killed by fragments of shrapnel from hand grenades or bombs. We had to identify the type of projectile and number of shots fired, the direction of the entry and exit point and the general trajectory. The degree of internal trauma was less significant.

The duties of the team members working in the mortuary were well defined. The forensic pathologist was in charge of each case, the scene-of-crime officer was handed all evidential material and the photographer documented all items of interest, including obvious areas of trauma. The anthropologists confirmed gender and estimated body height and age. In many cases, they had to reconstruct highly fragmented skulls, a result of close-range gunshot, to define the areas of trauma.

First we would x-ray the body bag to locate projectiles or shrapnel using an image intensifier. Being able to x-ray the body before the autopsy was a great help. The large, mobile x-ray machine displayed the images on a television monitor as we scanned each body. Three of us would put on the protective lead aprons (there were only three) and warn the staff that the x-ray beam was on. Someone would call out, 'Mind yer bits!' and those without aprons would duck behind those who had them on. We were able to x-ray a body bag in less than ten minutes by placing each body on a mobile table and advancing it forward and back beneath the beam. In this way, we could scan the entire body with minimum effort.

Having this machine made our job much easier. It would have been an almost impossible task to examine each body for the presence of projectiles and shrapnel if we had to do it by hand. It was also useful in checking the bodies for booby traps, but the only item that looked suspicious was a rectangular torch in the inside pocket of a victim's coat. Scotty was in charge of the x-ray machine. A radiographer from Yorkshire, he was also a British soldier and had done similar work in Bosnia. It was a pleasure to work with such experienced professionals. The whole examination procedure was smooth, greatly facilitated by the image intensifier, adequately equipped morgue and professional team.

I then followed the same procedure I used in East Timor. After opening the body bag, I estimated the age, height and gender of the victim. I looked for evidential material like blindfolds and ligatures and then I removed the clothing and gave it a preliminary wash to note its distinctive features. I next examined the body and bones for injuries, documenting each step and having it photographed.

I was the only forensic pathologist on location for the three-week period. All sixty-four bodies exhumed came under my care. The protocol adopted for the forensic work was strictly regimented and smooth, a tried and true system rather than the experimental form that had evolved in East Timor, so I was able to focus on performing the autopsies instead of finding ways to improvise. Following these procedures, we were able to fully examine and document the injuries of between four and five bodies a day. Although the workload was heavy and constant, I was able to work at a reasonable pace.

## THE AUTOPSIES

I began the external examination with an overall description of the body and items of clothing. This turned out to be a very protracted process. Unlike the victims of the Passabe massacre, who wore very little, most of these victims had on multiple layers of clothing. Many wore up to three pairs of trousers, three or four coats and several shirts and jumpers. This was possibly because they knew at the time of their abduction that they would not be returning to their homes soon, if at all. I also realised that the victims were probably very poor. Many of the clothes had been handed down and extensively repaired at home; they were covered with sewn-on patches, which made each item quite distinctive. This would help enormously in their identification on 'clothing days', when the washed and labelled clothes were laid out so that relatives could identify them and therefore possibly identify the victims. Once possible relatives were known, DNA specimens could be taken from the living, to be later compared to DNA specimens from the deceased. The identification of the victims is still going on today.

As in East Timor, a pro-forma was provided to document the description of the body, all trauma and the clothing. This process was much more lengthy in Kosova because I had to record the brand and size of each item of clothing and there was a great deal of it. In addition, I had to accurately chart the multitude of bullet entry and exit wounds and describe the passage of projectiles through each layer of clothing. I spent a lot of time at the end of each autopsy filling in the forms with every minute feature of the clothing in the hope that this would help relatives make positive identifications. I drew outlines of each piece of clothing to accurately display the entry and exit of bullets and the tearing from flying shrapnel fragments. I then illustrated body maps to show the exact anatomical relationship of the injuries identified. Once I had recorded all of these details, I documented the internal trauma. I was relieved that I didn't have to go into as much detail with the internal trauma; it was deemed to be much less useful because of the advanced degree of decomposition.

Once we had removed the clothing, we could perform the external examination. Most of the bodies were grossly decomposed. All overlying skin had undergone such alteration that in many cases I could not have identified immediate evidence of bullet trauma without the x-ray. Although the internal examination of the bodies showed extensive degradation of tissue, the telltale evidence of bullets and shrapnel could be readily identified. In particular, examining the skeleton gave a lot of information. I identified many cases where bullets had entered the back of the head or through the right or left temple. In many other cases, I identified rib damage and pelvic trauma caused by gunshots. Using x-rays, I was able to remove all projectiles and fragments of shrapnel from the body with great precision. They were later photographed and kept as evidence.

Over the course of the next fortnight, I examined all sixty-four bodies, although many more were being exhumed and stored. It was like working on some kind of ghastly process line. As the exhumation team worked through the mass grave, the bodies rapidly filled the mortuary refrigerators. We decided to store any surplus bodies in an above-ground refrigerated container for later examination. At the end of an average working day in the mortuary, a further twenty bodies would have been exhumed and awaiting examination. This made it necessary to call a temporary halt to the exhumations, which allowed us a short amount of catch-up time. We were under considerable pressure to examine as many bodies as we could in a day, but we were also aware that rushing the job could compromise the case and cause important evidence to be missed.

One extraordinary aspect of this mission was the items retrieved from the gravesite by the exhumation team that clearly did not relate directly to the period of ethnic cleansing and mass killings. We came across some very strange items. Medical refuse, anatomical specimens that had obviously been used for autopsy and anatomy demonstrations, and several large bags of miscellaneous rubbish were recovered. How they came to be there is a mystery. The gravesites must have been used as general dumping grounds for unwanted body parts, animal and human, when they were left unattended.

The first astonishing item we came across was a large plastic medical refuse bag containing approximately twenty foetuses of no more than eighteen weeks' gestation. We decided not to examine these small bodies, as clearly they had no bearing on the war crimes under investigation. Then several large green plastic bags were found in the depths of the grave. We emptied the contents onto the post-mortem table and were surprised to see several large chunks of decomposing red meat. The size of the meat fragments meant they were not human. There were more surprises. Another bag contained what appeared to be a pair of hands and feet. At first we thought that they might have been the remnants of torture involving the amputation of limbs, but upon closer examination we saw that they were in fact bear paws. Bear paws are very much like human hands and feet once the claws are lost, but the skeletal anatomy of the bear paw is subtly different to that of humans and the question was readily resolved by x-raying them. We concluded that this must be refuse after the butchering of a bear, perhaps during a hunting trip by one of the locals.

As in East Timor, most bodies exhumed were adult males, with no items that led to immediate identification. We found full identification on one body only. This appeared to be the property of a slain Serbian police officer in full uniform whose body was recovered along with the other Albanian victims. The presence of this body was puzzling. The examination disclosed a single shot to the back of his head, fired at close range. Perhaps he was the victim of a payback killing by angered Albanian citizens against the atrocities perpetrated against them. Sadly, at least one child was identified among the dead in the mass grave. All that was left of this small, pitiful body was a skull attached to a length of spine and some ribs. The remainder of the body had been blasted away, perhaps as the result of a hand grenade or bomb. Many of the bodies, although extensively shattered, also showed damage from fire. Perhaps they had been massacred in a building that the perpetrators had then set fire to before they removed the bodies and dumped them elsewhere. If so, we hoped that our work would ultimately render their attempt to destroy the victims' identities futile.

The degree of decomposition of the bodies generated a repulsive odour in the examination room, which ultimately filtered through the third floor of the building and down the lift-wells to the mortuary containment area. In between cases, while I wrote up my notes, I would light up my pipe. The tobacco I was smoking at the time was called Cherry Cavendish and I bought it from one of the local army stores. I was surprised that the team fully embraced this practice and, for the first time in my life, I was urged to please keep on smoking! They much preferred the smell of Cherry Cavendish tobacco to decomposing bodies.

The smell of decomposition that we had to endure in the morgue was nothing compared to the odours generated by the clothes being power washed in the carpark immediately in front of the university building. During my first week, team members laid out all the items of clothing we had gathered onto a large, blue plastic tarpaulin in front of the hospital. They used high-powered jet washers to blast away the mud and decomposed tissue sticking to the fabric. Clothes that had appeared to be dull and discoloured at autopsy were revealed to be brightly coloured and distinctive after cleaning. Team members then hung out the clothes to dry in the sun and later bagged, numbered and stored them in a steel container. It was bizarre for this job to be done out in the open, in full view of the visiting public. I have a vivid memory of a well-dressed young woman walking past the carpark when the clothes were being washed. The foul stench caused her to vomit in the carpark in front of the team. As a result, a corral made of steel posts and hessian bags was constructed to conceal the process. It hid the clothing from view, but it did nothing to reduce the overpowering odour.

We worked from eight o'clock in the morning until five or six o'clock in the evening, with a small midday break in between. We took our meals in the back of the 4WD parked in the parking bay of the hospital. Staff and visitors must have thought it strange to see people in their surgical scrubs eating sandwiches and having drinks while seated around and in the UN vehicle. At the end of a working day, our team would return to our home base and hope against hope that the hot water was working. We were often disappointed. Our only consolation for missing out on a hot shower at night was that we all smelled pretty much the same.

DOWN TIME

The days passed smoothly enough and the team worked well together and made good headway through the ever-mounting body count. The heavy workload reduced the chances for the team to have any real time off other than immediately out of hours. I was surprised at the large number of excellent restaurants in Pristina, all untouched by the war. On our first night we went to a restaurant called Mozart's. This was a real surprise. Although modest on the outside, inside it was extensively decorated with flower boxes, decorative lighting, a fountain and a beautifully designed open courtyard under the shade of a large tree. The range of food offered was extensive and it was absolutely delicious as well as being reasonably priced. We found that all the restaurants we patronised were cheap and excellent. It was easy to overindulge, so we decided that we should limit ourselves by having pizza on alternate nights, or eating in. Going out for a meal in pleasant surroundings provided a welcome relief to our grim duties during the day, although it seemed incongruous to be enjoying a meal after we had spent the day examining a seemingly endless procession of people who had been brutally murdered not far from where we were dining peacefully, and not so long ago.

The camaraderie within the team helped reduce the feelings of despair or dismay brought about by our daily work. On the nights we dined at home, we took it in turns to cook. Scotty would do a big shop, which would include lots of cheap, good wine. One night, a member of our exhumation team from Yorkshire, Mick Clarke, cooked a great Yorkshire pudding, and another night our American anthropologist did spaghetti bolognaise. Scotty and I created a 'Kosova Moment', a dessert consisting of ice cream, peach schnapps and strawberries. After the evening meal, we would adjourn to the roof garden for some drinks and have a chat about the day's activities. On some evenings, we would have a more formal debrief session where we would discuss our progress, identify any problems and discuss ways to solve them. The evening temperatures made it a very pleasant way of unwinding at the end of a busy day, although the tranquillity was occasionally punctured by the burst of automatic gunfire. There were occasional reports of shooting, particularly at UN vehicles, during our stay. The tranquillity was also punctuated on a regular basis by the Muslim call to prayer over the loudspeakers attached to the minarets of a nearby mosque.

As in East Timor, I was greatly frustrated in trying to phone home. Our mobile phones were unable to pick up any local signals; even our British colleagues had this problem. I can remember one frustrating evening, speed-dialling my home number again and again. Some time after midnight, the phone finally displayed a dial signal and for the first time in ten days I was able to tell my wife that I'd arrived safely and bring her up to date on our progress.

One night, a member of the team put on a video called *The Body Hunters*, an English television program that documented the activities of a previous British forensic team in Kosova. This story detailed the tragic search by a family for their missing family members and their interactions with the forensic teams. It graphically portrayed the human misery behind the crimes we were investigating. It added the very human dimension to the war crime investigations, one that we didn't usually allow ourselves to dwell on. Rather, we would focus on how our work would ultimately help to return the dead to their families. There wasn't a dry eye in the room by the end of this very moving account.

Finally, the day came for one full day of rest and relaxation. There was some talk that the team would take a day trip to the Greek coast, but this was later changed to an outing to the nearby Alps. We travelled to Prizren, the ancient capital of Kosova located several hours' drive from Pristina. We passed through magnificent scenery, including steep mountain ranges, deep ravines and fast-flowing rivers. Prizren is a beautiful city, with fine Byzantine architecture and an ancient ruin on a nearby hill. It is also noted for its quality silver jewellery. A beautiful stream, spanned by several stone bridges, winds its way through the centre of the town. Even here, several buildings had been reduced to rubble during the recent conflict. After enjoying the afternoon sun and a fine meal, the team decided to take the scenic route through the mountains back to Pristina. The day was not to be incident free. Half an hour into the journey, the road traffic up one of the hills came to a sudden halt. We assumed there had been a road accident, but sadly, information was passed down the line that a child had been injured by a landmine blast. Our immediate response was to offer our medical and nursing assistance, but the news filtered back that the child had died.

The number of landmines in Kosova is unknown, but there are probably hundreds of thousands. Many farmers find live ammunition and mines in their fields and place them on the roadside in the hope that they will be found by the authorities and disarmed. In this instance, the young child had probably picked up the device and it had exploded, killing him instantly. This was a very sad end to what was otherwise a wonderful day. It seemed that we could not even have one day that was not overshadowed by death.

## THE BOMB GARDEN

A couple of days before leaving Kosova, the team was asked to attend the 'bomb garden' in Pristina. The bomb garden is run by the UN to show staff the unexploded ammunition and mines that are scattered throughout the countryside and forested areas. The large anti-tank mines that are hidden in main roads are not the only mines. A large number of mines are small and well camouflaged, designed to kill or maim whoever walks by them. I had noticed warning signs with pictures of the types of ordnance to beware of in forested areas surrounding Pristina. It is an unwritten law that anyone finding a bomb will place a signal of some sort close to the spot where it was found. The signal may consist of a piece of ribbon tied onto a tree, or perhaps a pile of stones indicating the general direction of the unexploded ordnance.

The first part of the half-day program was a short presentation by one of the ordnance experts. The second part was a walk through the bomb garden, a piece of land overgrown with shrubs and trees, with a derelict building and several car bodies, that was filled with dummy mines. The instructor asked us to closely examine an area of grass less than a metre square to find the trigger of a landmine. I looked and looked in this area and couldn't see any trigger device. He then suggested I examine a smaller part of the same area and concentrate my attention on the centre of it. Again, I couldn't identify any trigger. The instructor then directed my search to an even smaller patch, but I was still unsuccessful. He finally pointed out a single small green structure about the size and thickness of a blade of grass. This was the trigger to a buried landmine. I was shocked at how easily these deadly devices can be missed. Having failed so dismally at bomb detection, I wondered whether I had inadvertently strayed near any during my time in Kosova.

The landmines in Kosova are designed to detonate immediately on contact. It is a myth that you should stand very still and wait to be rescued when you realise you are standing on a mine. Another device demonstrated to us was the so-called 'bounding bomb'. This terrible device is designed to spring upwards to head or chest height and then to fragment in a radial fashion. Multiple fragments of metal will then fly in all directions for a distance of approximately one hundred and fifty metres. This device was designed to maim troops rather than kill, thus creating a logistical nightmare for any advancing soldiers on patrol. Many of the injuries in the bodies examined made no sense until I saw these devices. In several cases, I identified widely dispersed shrapnel fragments in the chest, pelvic area and legs of many of the victims. Seeing the way that this device explodes and fragments explained some of these injuries.

Cluster bombs are also scattered everywhere throughout the country. These bombs are the size of 44-gallon drums, and are designed to burst open when released from an aircraft, leaving the individual bomblets on parachutes to explode on impact. As their fail rate is up to fifteen per cent, live cluster bombs are everywhere.

They look like toys and are picked up by children with fatal consequences.

The ingenuity and range of devices was staggering. The irony was that we were given this very informative half-day program of bomb awareness two days before we were due to leave Kosova. I could have done with this information at the beginning rather than at the end of my tour of duty.

## MISSION ACCOMPLISHED

On the final day of my tour, I was invited to be part of a helicopter crew on an aerial surveillance of a Serb-held area to photograph tracts of land showing disturbed areas of soil that might indicate mass gravesites. We met the white Super Puma helicopter at the airfield quite near to the destroyed Serb barracks and fuel dump. Our helicopter pilot was an Australian airman. Although no stranger to helicopter transport, the large, heavy calibre machine-gun hanging from the door openings made me wonder whether this was a good idea. The crew took photographs of areas of farmland, including a small church with several rectangular areas of disturbed soil. These would be submitted to the intelligence sections of the UN to decide whether to investigate these sites further. We then returned to Pristina. On the way back, our pilot casually asked if there were any novice passengers in the back. Several of passengers raised their hands, and, with a wicked glint in his eye, he banked the helicopter steeply, creating an effect like a roller coaster. This feeling was both exhilarating and terrifying.

At the end of the tour, I had successfully completed all sixty-four post-mortem examinations and was delighted by the work of the team. Having all the professional personnel, as well as the added luxury of real-time radiology, had meant the examination process ran almost seamlessly. I collated my handwritten reports to be sent back to Britain where the data would be put into an information base for collation by liaison officers. The database will contain all data on missing persons, as well as the forensic information from the investigation. This vital information gained by the team would be essential to identifying the victims and will be part of the brief of evidence for the prosecution of crimes against humanity.

I had made many friends during my three-week tour and it was a very sad day when we parted company. Many of us still exchange Christmas cards, and Scotty has become a firm friend. Several years after this trip, I convinced Scotty and his lovely wife Anne, to visit Australia by sending them some tourist videos. We had the privilege of looking after them for a week or so during the Victorian leg of their first visit to Australia, which they enjoyed immensely. They plan to return for another visit.

After an evening of packing luggage and souvenirs, several of us returned to Skopje in Macedonia. At the airport, some of us said our good-byes while the remainder of the team gathered for the ordeal of visa endorsement and clearance. Several hours later we arrived at Heathrow Airport and one of our team members who acted as a scene-of-crime officer was gracious enough to drive me to my hotel in London. Although I had appreciated the relatively comfortable accommodation in Pristina, it was wonderful indeed to settle back into the luxury of a good hotel with a guaranteed supply of hot water. The flight home was uneventful and I once again enjoyed the benefits of business class travel. I returned to the VIFM with many rolls of undeveloped film, all of which produced fine examples of the post-mortem work, as well as capturing many fond memories of good times had and new friends found. I had brought a copy of *The Body Hunters* video home and showed it to my colleagues at the VIFM. They watched the program in stunned silence, overcome by the tragedy of what they were seeing.

Before leaving Kosova, I had asked the team leader, Ron Turnbull, whether I was likely to have to return to the international court in The Hague to give personal evidence. He replied that it was almost certain that I would be required. The evidence of the forensic team has been tendered, but I have not yet been asked to give evidence, though criminal proceedings into the crimes in the former Yugoslavia have been underway for some time. I am assuming that the documentary evidence submitted is considered sufficient.

Despite the creation of the International Criminal Tribunal for the former Yugoslavia (ICTY), not many war criminals have been convicted for their involvement in the atrocities that were committed. Former President Slobodan Milosevic went on trial in February 2002. He was charged with sixty-six counts including genocide and crimes against humanity for his alleged key role in directing the forces as head of the Federal Republic of Yugoslavia (FRY) as they executed a campaign of terror and violence directed at Kosova Albanian civilians in 1998 to 1999. He was extradited to the war crimes tribunal in The Hague, but the trial has suffered many disruptions and delays due to Milosevic's ill health. He is representing himself, and the defence case, which began in August 2004, is still ongoing. As in East Timor, there is much frustration within the international community with this situation, and fear that many of the worst perpetrators will not be called to justice for the atrocities committed in Kosova.

# FOUR

# EAST TIMOR
## OCTOBER 2000

In late September 2000, I received a phone call from a member of the Special Crimes Investigation Unit (SCIU) in East Timor requesting my presence. There were two bodies requiring examination as a matter of urgency. One was a slain militiaman and the other the body of a man found dead on the beach in suspicious circumstances. In what was now becoming something of a routine procedure, I spent the next few days involved in the United Nations (UN) contractual arrangements. Once the details were confirmed, I flew to Darwin for an overnight stay before catching the UN C-130 Hercules the following morning. I had been warned before leaving to confirm my aircraft seat from the UN office in Darwin. After checking in, I strolled around the corner to the UN building to identify my name on the manifest. To my horror, it wasn't there. The UN staff lacked the authority to allocate a seat, so I spent the next few hours on the phone frantically trying to reach key people in East Timor to authorise my flight. It wasn't until after midnight that I finally got the problem resolved. Greatly relieved,

I got a good night's sleep and the next morning I caught a small mini-bus with several others. After loading up our baggage onto a small trailer behind the bus, we set off for the departure lounge of the Darwin International Airport. All UN flights, Hercules or otherwise, now departed from Darwin Airport rather than the RAAF base. One small consolation was that we were able to buy duty-free goods on our way to East Timor. The trip in the Hercules was uneventful and I felt like an old hand at this. Like the other seasoned Hercules travellers, I had even brought my own ear protection.

As we touched down at Dili Airport, I noticed many changes since my previous visit. The airport was functioning less as a military base and now more closely resembled a small commercial airfield like those in Fiji or Vanuatu. The large camouflaged fuel dump was still there, but there were far fewer military helicopters, heavily armed personnel and army trucks. Several UN workers were waiting for me and they promptly escorted me to the mortuary. There was little time to find accommodation or exchange pleasantries; this was an urgent, short stay and the introductions and brief were businesslike.

The mortuary was much as I had remembered it, though I noted that there was more equipment. The international forensic staff who had followed my first trip had each contributed in some way to the facility, so the mortuary was evolving in the right direction. I had been told of this and so hadn't thought it necessary to bring my own supplies. Several filing cabinets, desks and chairs had also been installed. The trestle table that supported our pro-formas and camera equipment had finally been replaced by a more robust structure. In addition, the mortuary now had two young East Timorese female assistants, Laura Maia and Filomena Gomes. The UN had enlisted them to assist with autopsies and body reconstruction and they had been given some basic training in this area.

Although their English skills were limited, we had little trouble communicating and they were both eager and enthusiastic. Laura was hoping to get into medical school. We brought the post-mortem instruments out of storage and I checked them to make sure they were sharp enough. Everything appeared to be fine and it was time to get started without delay.

The first case involved a militiaman who had allegedly been shot by a peacekeeper in West Timor. Incidents of conflict after the civil war between members of the peacekeeping forces and the militia groups caused much alarm in the community and were investigated closely. For this reason, I had to perform a detailed post-mortem examination. The body was waiting in the refrigerator. We brought the victim out and I made some preliminary observations. The refrigerated container had performed its function well; the body showed only the earliest signs of decomposition. The man had on a t-shirt with 'Autonomy' written across the front. Around his neck he wore a string necklace with a plastic container attached. It looked like one used for storing film. This container was filled with white powder. I sent it off for analysis, as it was possible that the substance was some kind of amphetamine. I had heard stories that amphetamine use was common among the members of the militia groups. It was also possible that it was the ground lime used to chew betel nut that locals often carried around with them.

This case did not present any immediate forensic difficulties. I began a very detailed external examination of this slim but well-nourished man. He had been shot twice in the upper chest. The bullet entry and exit wounds were immediately obvious. The shots had caused several secondary exit wounds through the right chest. One of the bullets had created a further injury through the upper right arm and extensive disruption to the heart and lungs. The second projectile had entered the left upper arm and passed into the chest, causing further extensive internal trauma. There was also a large gaping wound over the left groin. As I searched for the possible cause of this injury, I wondered whether a further bullet had possibly detonated a rifle grenade that may have been attached to his waist. The ragged, untidy laceration over the left groin suggested an exploding device may have been attached to the man's belt. This seemed like a plausible explanation and I managed to get the hospital to perform an x-ray examination, which showed multiple small, metal fragments near his pubic bone that had not entered the abdominal cavity.

I coordinated the internal and external photographs and recorded the findings on my dictaphone. Once I got home my stenographer would transcribe the details and email the final autopsy report to the UN by the end of the week. I thought this would be a more efficient system than using the pro-formas provided. As I dictated the findings and summary comments, Laura and Filomena reconstructed the body meticulously. While I am reasonably capable in the area of post-mortem body reconstruction, I am always happy to delegate this task.

I decided to examine the second case the following day and to spend the remainder of the afternoon trying to find accommodation. I asked around and the UN staff suggested that I try the *Hotel Olympia*. This is a large 'floating hotel' that follows the UN around to troubled areas, enabling international staff to be easily accommodated offshore. I remembered Matt Skinner telling me about the *Olympia* as he had stayed on it in February and March of that year. Once the initial novelty had worn off, he had found the experience quite soul destroying and described it as a floating prison ship. As I looked at the ship from the shore, I immediately understood what he meant. The large, flat platform was heavily decked by a multitude of containers, all connected by open walkways. The containers could accommodate several hundred people at one time. There was also a large galley area and dining hall. I checked in through the security gangway leading from the shore to the *Olympia* and was shown to my small room. The bed was comfortable and there was an ensuite bathroom, but it was very spartan in all other respects. I could not imagine staying on this ship for more than a few days. Matt was right, it was just like being in a floating penitentiary. I was told I would be bunking with another UN worker, but he never showed up, so at least I had the small room to myself. As I lay in my bed after the day's work, I could think of nothing worse than spending time somewhere like this through choice, as you would on a cruise ship. Although I was grateful for the immediate offer of fully paid accommodation and a well-cooked meal, I couldn't wait to get off it.

As my stay in East Timor on this occasion was only for two working days, I decided that it would be a waste of valuable time to go through the lengthy UN induction process. The induction could take up all my working time, as many people in many departments would need to see me to sign many forms. As full contractual arrangements had been made before my departure, it had been agreed that it would be more efficient if I bypassed this bureaucratic process. This attempt to avoid the system would have major ramifications on my third visit.

## THE CASE OF THE POISONOUS CRAB

The following morning, I was given detailed information about the second body waiting for an autopsy. This was to prove one of the most baffling and challenging cases of my professional career to date and would lead to the publication of a co-authored article expounding the case as a world first. British civilian police officers

Sue Pollard and Brendan Thoroughgood outlined the circumstances surrounding the case. The victim was a thirty-two year old East Timorese man, who had been found dead on Behau Beach on 1 October. The young man had met up with about a dozen friends on the beach earlier in the day. About an hour later, he had caught some crabs and possibly a sea cucumber. He boiled up the crabs to make soup and ate it with the sea cucumber. After finishing the meal, he joined in with the group and drank a couple of cans of beer. According to the witnesses, everything appeared to be completely normal. A short while later, the young man vomited into the sea. Saying that he felt exhausted, he lay down under a tree and fell asleep. Around midday, one of his friends tried to rouse the apparently sleeping man and found him dead.

There was no evidence from this story that this man had been involved in any sort of violent altercation and his sudden death seemed inexplicable. But upon hearing the story, the family alleged that a homicide had taken place and had implicated his boss. The post-mortem examination was considered a high priority, as the police had no evidence of murder or any alternative theory.

Again, Filomena and Laura were there to assist and detailed photographs were taken at each stage. The external examination showed no evidence of any trauma or foul play. As there was no evidence of violence, the remaining possibilities were death by natural causes, or, as alleged by the family, a case of poisoning. I hoped the internal examination would yield more clues, but I could find no abnormalities. None of the deceased's internal organs showed evidence of any significant, naturally occurring disease. His heart, lungs and brain looked completely normal to the naked eye. I identified several subtle changes, including mildly congested lungs. The lungs appear mildly congested after death in virtually all bodies, so this didn't help. The blood vessels surrounding the brain were engorged, which is generally regarded as a phase of acute cardiac failure.

After failing to find any evidence pointing to the cause of death, I had to conclude that it was an unascertained death. This was highly unsatisfactory from all points of view, but I had very little to tell the police investigating officers. I could only recommend that further tests be undertaken. As there are no forensic laboratory facilities in East Timor, all specimens would have to be sent back to Australia for toxicological analysis. There were no appropriate collecting tubes or jars in the mortuary, so I needed to improvise. Since my previous visit, the distinctive domed building across the road from the agricultural college had been turned into a field hospital. I ran over there and, after some fast talking, managed to acquire several small plain blood-collecting tubes from them. I also managed to find some small containers in the back of the mortuary storage facility that were appropriate for storing solid material. I took samples of blood, urine, bile, gastric content and liver for toxicological analysis. Normally, formalin is used as a preservative for solid tissues, but there was none to be found at the mortuary, so I used methylated spirits diluted to seventy per cent strength with tap water. I set aside small samples of brain, heart, lung, liver, kidney, spleen and pancreas for fixation and later examination under the microscope. Lastly, I wrote a letter of request to accompany the specimens and the civilian police organised for them to be transferred to Australia for analysis. I dictated this puzzling case into my dictaphone and issued a preliminary report. That completed the two cases, but the story certainly didn't end there. Rather surprising findings would eventually be discovered after the samples were analysed.

I spent the following night in my small, cell-like container on the *Olympia*. The next morning, as I was taking a shower, large volumes of stagnant water percolated up through the drain. As I checked out, I mentioned to the man on the desk that it looked like they had a significant problem with their plumbing. He seemed to take the news casually and replied was that it was not uncommon and that it would be looked into at some stage. Thankfully, it wasn't my problem and I left. As I walked along the gangplank to the shore, I was struck by the panoramic view of the magnificent Government House. A backdrop of lush green foliage and rolling hills framed this building. What struck me was how Government House stood out still intact among the burnt-out ruins right next to it. I was reminded of the story Shayne had told me, that the militia were intercepted right at that point by INTERFET troops. Had the militia not been stopped there, Government House too would have been destroyed.

As I was putting my gear together to head back to the airport, Sue asked me what we should do with the remnants of crab shell that had been retrieved from the cooking pot that the dead man had used to cook up his soup on the beach. My first instinct was to say that they would not be relevant in this case and that I couldn't see how they could be implicated. Intuitively, I thought that cooking and eating a few small crabs could surely not be dangerous, let alone fatal. But a nagging doubt in my mind told me that these, too, should be packaged up and sent to Melbourne to be frozen until the preliminary toxicology report came through. Later, I was glad that I didn't follow my instincts on this one.

I returned to Melbourne to my normal duties and awaited the results of the toxicology report. After about six weeks, the report crossed my desk. The results were disappointing. A small amount of alcohol was detected, in keeping with the story that the deceased had consumed several small cans of beer on the beach before he died. I noted the complete absence of commonly prescribed medications, as well as illicit drugs such as amphetamines, heroin and marijuana. This report verified the initial finding of an unascertained case and I sent back an interim report to East Timor to this effect.

For some reason, the crab shells still played on my mind. I wondered whether it was possible that these crabs may have caused this young man's death. Surely not. I had certainly never encountered anything similar, or read about anything of this kind before. In cases like this, a forensic pathologist needs to think laterally and well out of the square. I consulted a colleague of mine at the VIFM, Dr Melanie Archer, a forensic entomologist and zoologist by training. She suggested that I take the crab shells to the Department of Zoology at the University of Melbourne. I followed her advice, and took them in to be examined by Dr Gary Poore, who was at that time Curator of Crustaceans. Gary identified this crab as being *Zosimus aeneus*. To my great surprise, he said this was a species of toxic crab and that the flesh of the crab may contain substances known as saxitoxin and tetrodotoxin. These lethal substances have been known to cause death within several hours. Human fatalities from eating this family of crab, Xanthidae, have been documented in Japan, the Philippines, Mauritius, Vanuatu and other Pacific islands. There were even documented anecdotal reports of suicide by eating this small crab. This was certainly a revelation to me and was also largely unknown in forensic circles.

The problem now was to confirm that the man had died from eating this crab. Gary suggested that I consult Dr Lyndon Llewellyn at the Australian Institute of Marine Science in Townsville, Queensland. Lyndon is a renowned expert in the field of marine toxins and has published widely in this area. I phoned him and outlined the case to him. To say that he became immediately animated by this potential case would be an understatement. Barely containing his

excitement, he asked me whether I still had the biological specimens from the autopsy. When I said I did, he said that if we could
prove beyond doubt that the toxin was present in the biological
samples as well as in the crab flesh remnants, then this would be
the first fully documented case worldwide of death caused by the
ingestion of toxic crabs. It finally seemed that we were getting
closer to solving this mysterious death.

I sent the crab shell remnants, which had turned a bright
red from the cooking process, and all body fluid and tissue samples
to Lyndon. The analysis of saxitoxin is an elaborate and difficult
process and the methodology required was not yet in place. Lyndon
informed me that it could possibly take several months before he
could establish and validate methods to prove our case beyond
doubt. I put the case to one side in my mind and returned to my
normal duties. Several months later, Lyndon called from Townsville
again in a very excited state. He told me that he had identified
elevated levels of saxitoxin present in the crab remnants. In addition,
he had found markedly elevated levels of the toxin present in all the
tissue specimens retained from the autopsy. This was proof positive
that this unexplained death was in fact due to paralytic shellfish
poisoning. The tragedy in this case was simply that saxitoxin is
both water-soluble and heat stable. In short, the worst possible
scenario had occurred as the young man cooked up his lunch on
the beach. By making a soup of these small creatures, the toxin had
leached out from the flesh and had been preserved. As this substance
is a potent neurotoxin, the young man would have slipped into a
coma and ultimately died of respiratory paralysis.

As a direct result of this astounding finding, I was finally able
to send a definitive autopsy report to East Timor. Lyndon and
I and several other co-workers published a paper on this case in the
international peer-reviewed journal *Toxicon*. The paper outlined in

great detail the physiological actions of these toxins on the nervous system and the methods that had been devised to detect them. Further research indicates that between sixty-five and one hundred per cent of *Zosimus aeneus* crabs collected from regional areas may contain lethal quantities of saxitoxin. To confuse things, however, a collection of crabs from one area may contain several that are completely harmless. To complicate matters further, the concentration of toxin within the flesh may vary according to the season.

I was left wondering how many other unsuspecting East Timorese people had died in a similar fashion. I suspected that there could have been many such deaths. Perhaps as such communities become more westernised, traditional knowledge of the characteristics and peculiarities of local species could be lost. As a result, the people may no longer be aware of how to cook and handle these seemingly small, innocuous creatures. This information may help explain other sudden and unexpected deaths in otherwise healthy people in this area.

I felt that to walk away from this situation would have been wrong, so I attempted to generate a public awareness campaign in East Timor. I spoke to many people in the SCIU and was given all assurances that the information would be passed on to the relevant authorities within government. Emails months later suggested that nothing had happened. The only resort now was to go to the top. With pen in hand, I wrote a detailed letter and report to the newly elected President Xanana Gusmao imploring him to examine this case and speak to the relevant minister so that a public awareness campaign could be instigated. I imagined posters or placards with a picture of the crab and warning signs in the various languages used in East Timor. Sadly, nothing ever came of this initiative until a unique opportunity presented itself in December 2002.

# FIVE

# EAST TIMOR
## JANUARY 2001 AND JULY 2002

Since my first mission in East Timor, many international pathologists had volunteered to participate in forensic investigations on a
roster basis. My name was down on the list of available volunteers
and I was active in seeking overseas work. In the middle of January
2001, I received a call from the Special Crimes Investigaton Unit
(SCIU) in Dili to inquire whether I was available for two fresh
cases that required immediate examination. I was also asked if I
would be interested in participating in several exhumations in the
highlands in the middle of the island towards the south coast. The
idea of venturing outside of Dili was exciting, as up till then I had
only been to the capital and part of the north coast.

## JANUARY 2001

I flew from Melbourne to Darwin, then from Darwin to Dili on
the United Nations (UN) Hercules C-130. Brian Clark met me at
Dili airport. Brian is a New Zealand civilian police officer who had

been seconded to Dili six weeks previously to coordinate post-mortem examinations and exhumations. Brian is a colourful character and, like all UN members I had had the pleasure to work with, a very good natured and easygoing chap.

As usual, the first concern was accommodation. I declined the offer of the *Hotel Olympia*. Since the referendum, several small hotels had sprung up and were all doing surprisingly well. There were still enough UN personnel needing accommodation and the occasional tourist would venture into the country to explore the beautiful highland areas. The Dili Lodge Hotel was located a short drive from the airport and within walking distance of the Agricultural College, which now housed the SCIU and mortuary facility. This would be convenient as I wouldn't have to rely on daily lifts to and from the mortuary. The hotel was made up of several rows of construction huts that had been linked together. In many ways it was similar to the *Hotel Olympia*, but on the ground. There was the deluxe room, which included a small ensuite toilet and bathroom, or the standard room with shared bathroom facilities. The containers, although small, were adequately furnished with a comfortable bed, an air-conditioner, a desk and a chair. There was an onsite restaurant that served quite good food at a reasonable price. Several of the UN personnel were living at the hotel, but most of the guests were construction workers from Darwin who had been brought over to rebuild the city.

As this stay would be approximately sixteen days, it was necessary to go through the usual UN induction process. There was no escaping it this time. My previous trip of three days had not gone unnoticed by the UN personnel department. Upon presenting myself to the coordinations building, I was eyeballed by the personnel manager, who said, 'You! We've been waiting for you to come back. You never inducted the last time you were here!' I tried to explain why, but my explanation fell on deaf ears. So I underwent what had become an incredibly laborious induction process that lasted two days. I should have known that there would be no escaping the UN bureaucracy as I also signed in and out to cover the paperwork that should have been completed during my last short trip.

The city of Dili is widespread and, unfortunately for me and other UN personnel, many of the stations that needed to be checked in and out of as part of the induction process were spread out all around the city. Brian offered to drive me to the various locations so I could sign in for the car that I never drove and take possession of a radio that I would never use and the firearm that I would never carry. I was given a pro-forma with at least twelve stations that needed to be sighted and they had to be sighted in order. You were not able to skip a station if the person you needed to see was not available when you arrived. UN personnel were often away from their desks for an extended period during lunchtime. After this very frustrating and lengthy process was complete, I was able to settle down into the work I had been brought over for.

Since my first mission to East Timor, when Shayne, Matt and I had completed the first autopsies at the makeshift morgue, there had been continuous improvements in the facilities and staffing. An additional technician had joined the team since my last visit. Francelino Freitas, a young local man, had had some previous experience in the operating theatre of one of the local hospitals. He was therefore well suited to mortuary work. Happily, Laura and Filomena were still there and they gave me a warm welcome. I was also delighted to see Wayne Fee, who had been part of the original International Force for East Timor (INTERFET) contingent. Since I had seen him last, he had shed his soldier's uniform and had become a permanent member of the SCIU based in Dili. Another bonus was the presence of a fully-fledged physical anthropologist, Anahi Ginarte, who had joined the team on rotation. A pleasant young woman, Anahi was part of the Argentine Forensic Anthropology Team and came to us with wide experience in anthropology as it applies to the investigation of atrocities and mass killings.

There were two fresh cases in the refrigerator requiring immediate attention. Both bodies were part of the same case. Apparently there had been an altercation between a security guard and a local. Witnesses said that they had seen a local man chase the guard to the end of a pier and force him to jump into the water, although it was well known that the guard was unable to swim. The body was found in the water some time later. This autopsy showed the classic internal findings consistent with death by drowning. I then began the examination of the second body, the alleged assailant. The external examination showed slight blunt trauma over the right frontal scalp area and to the left side of the chest, but this was not lethal damage. The internal findings of this body were again in keeping with drowning and external injuries indicated that some kind of struggle could have preceded his falling in the water. Both of these autopsies were straightforward and the procedures were completed smoothly.

The plan was that after lunch the following day, Wayne, Brian and I would venture into the mountainous areas of the middle part of East Timor to exhume three bodies. The first point of call was a village called Ainaro. We checked the map on the wall of the SCIU office, and located Ainaro about sixty kilometres due south of Dili. We calculated that the drive would take no more than an hour or two. How wrong we were! Due to the mountainous terrain and narrow roads, the trip took well over four hours. As we drove along the winding road from Dili into the mountains, the coastline of Dili and the ships in the harbour came into view, as well as beautiful Atauro Island to the north of Dili. Once we had travelled about twenty kilometres out of Dili, the landscape changed dramatically. The terrain became extremely mountainous, with sheer rock cliffs and ravines on either side of us. In many parts, the road was merely a dust-covered goat track, spanning one peak to another. The mountain ranges in this area measure up to about two and a half thousand metres above sea level. Even at the altitude we were travelling, the air was cool and thin. We stopped along the way to take photos of the panoramic views of the mountains.

At mid-morning, we entered a town called Maubisse, famous for its local coffee. The road into town was flanked on either side by dense coffee plantations. We decided to stop for a coffee break, so we pulled over to one side and entered a small shop across the road from the local market. The shop was a small general store with tables and chairs. The lighting was very poor and there was no ventilation, so it was stifling inside. The coffee, though, was magic. We stocked up on cans of Coke to see us through the rest of the trip and pressed on. Several parts of the track were exceedingly difficult to pass. Fortunately for us, the monsoon rains had passed. The track was covered in fine brown dust and there were occasional gigantic potholes. Along the way, we encountered a local car that had become completely bogged down in one of the deep potholes. We stopped to help and were able to extract the thankful driver with our winch.

## AINARO

Eventually, we reached the village of Ainaro. This village showed evidence of destruction by the militia. We passed many burnt-out houses and many of the larger buildings in the centre of the town had been destroyed. We called in at the local police station to show our papers and authorisation for exhumation that had been granted by the investigating judge at the District Court of Dili. This done, we made our way to our lodgings in the rapidly fading light. Our lodgings were in a small, fortress-like building at the end of a steep, winding track into the dense jungle. This building was whitewashed and showed Spanish-Portuguese influence. It had been used as a military hospital during the Second World War and was around a hundred years old. Several civilian police and UN workers had already become well entrenched in the many rooms of this sprawling old building. The floor was covered with previously assembled mosquito domes and a well-laden kitchen and pantry had been set up towards the back. It was a pretty good set-up, actually. There was a reasonable sound system, a good selection of CDs and a small television. Australian and New Zealand flags hung in many of the doorways. After the introductions, I put up my mosquito dome, placed it over a small groundsheet and blew up the air mattress and pillow. We had a hearty meal of baked beans on toast and went straight to bed to be ready for the early start next morning.

The next morning, we set off back to the village of Ainaro. Several members of the UN Civilian Police Force met us there. Before long, a throng of locals had gathered to watch us unpack our equipment. The gravesites to be exhumed were legitimate burials of two men who had allegedly been shot to death during the conflict. The UN police led us to a rectangular open area next to one of the small houses on the main street. The soil was a very firm, rich red-brown clay and was overgrown by tall, bright-orange marigolds. The vague outlines of the graves were pointed out to us. They had been marked by rows of small pebbles. Many of the locals insisted on helping with the digging and we were happy for them to. We told them that they must stop digging at the very first sign that the coffins had been reached. The graves lay side by side and it took several hours to dig down the two metres or so of firm soil before the coffin lids were exposed. Wayne and Brian jumped into the pit to remove the soil from around the coffins and then carefully placed ropes beneath them so that they could be lifted above the ground. The coffins, although small, were made of dense, hard dark-brown wood and were surprisingly heavy. Once we had removed them, we enclosed them in blue plastic body bags and loaded them onto the back of the tray-truck. By this time, most of the village had come to observe our work, including the immediate members of the victims' families.

Before we headed off, the villagers asked us if we would like to sit and eat a small meal with them. Within moments, they had placed a low table in front of us and covered it with a pristine, white tablecloth. They placed small dishes of food before us, along with a white porcelain teapot, milk jug and coffee cups with saucers. This immaculate porcelain tea set was a surprise, as it was at such odds with the abject poverty that surrounded us. It was a touching gesture and we well and truly appreciated it. We had our afternoon tea and assured the family that the bodies would be returned to them by the end of the following week.

## ANIMAL SACRIFICE IN CASSA

We then set off for Cassa, a small village located approximately thirty kilometres due south of Ainaro. A body was apparently buried in an open quarry-like area off the road to the right about four kilometres out of Cassa. In contrast to the trip to Ainaro the previous day, this was an easy drive through rolling plains, open fields and paddy fields. Occasionally, we saw a water buffalo wallowing in one of the large mudholes to escape the heat and flies. Once at Cassa, we found where the body was quickly enough. We headed off towards one edge of the quarry where we were told we would find a small mound of stones that indicated the location of the grave. This was a secondary burial site, as the body had originally been found some distance away after the militia had attacked the village. We had no trouble finding the mound and, after taking GPS readings and overall photography, we got our tools from the back of the tray-truck to begin digging. In my eagerness to help, I began setting aside some of the rocks from the top of the pile. Wayne abruptly halted me, warning me that there were scorpions everywhere. To demonstrate, he carefully lifted one of the stones with the corner of his shovel and, sure enough, at least half a dozen small brown scorpions scattered from the daylight. As they were potentially lethal, I took the point and wore heavy gloves to remove the rest of the rocks.

Before long, we came to a white rice sack buried about half a metre from the surface. We carefully removed it and opened it. Inside were the bones of the slain local villager. By this time, inevitably, many family members and local villagers had arrived. It seemed fitting at this point to ask those present whether they would like to say a few words over the body. Wayne, being a veteran of around a hundred exhumations, had warned me that occasionally the local villagers would sacrifice a small dog over the grave before the body was removed, although he had never actually witnessed this. He advised me that if this should take place, I was to look either straight ahead or down to the ground and not show any body language indicating abhorrence or disgust, as this would deeply offend the locals.

A man stepped forward from the gathering. He was carrying a small hessian bag and a length of iron pipe. He reached into the bag and lifted out a small, light-brown puppy, no more than a few weeks old. The puppy was lifted above the grave while prayers were said in a language that we could not understand. After the short prayer, he struck the puppy on the back of the head with the iron pipe. Another man stepped forward with a t-shirt that had belonged to the slain victim. He produced a sharpened shaft of bamboo and plunged it deep into the gravesite. He then wrapped the t-shirt around the top of the stick. Blood from the puppy's head was then dripped onto the garment. This animist ritual was conducted to secure the spirit of the deceased. The locals believed that without this ritual, the spirit would be free to wander while the body was taken to Dili for examination. This may seem to be curious behaviour coming from devout Catholics, but the locals seem to be able to blend their Catholic and animist beliefs and rituals without any problem. While we were a little taken aback by the killing of the puppy in front of us, I don't believe it suffered. It was a swift, merciful killing and it didn't even have time to yelp or cry. Having completed their duty, the gathering turned away and walked back towards the road.

We placed the rice sack containing the bones into a larger body bag and loaded it onto the back of the tray-truck with the other two victims. After a short coffee break, we headed back to Dili. It was dark when we arrived some four hours later. The crew dropped me off at the Dili Lodge Hotel. After having a quick shower and a change of clothes, I went over to the restaurant for a bite to eat. We were due to repeat the whole process the following day, so I turned in early.

## AINARO AGAIN

At seven o'clock the following morning, the crew arrived to pick me up. We were headed back to Ainaro to exhume two more bodies buried in a conventional cemetery. The UN 4WD tray-truck traced the same route as the previous day, stopping briefly at Maubisse for a coffee break, but this time in a beautiful Portuguese resort, which is a prominent feature of the area. The large white building is perched on top of a small, conical hill, like a miniature version of Mt Fuji. The approach to the resort was by a narrow causeway from the main road. This resort was also renowned for its coffee and we enjoyed a brief rest and cup of coffee before continuing. On our arrival at Ainaro, we once again met up with the local police officer to show our papers and authorisation for the exhumation. We then made our way to the large cemetery that was filled with many ornate headstones and overgrown with weeds. The heat and humidity of the day were extreme and swarms of mosquitoes descended upon us. We drove the truck down a small path to the middle of the cemetery and were shown the sites of the two graves. As these were Christian burials, we expected the coffins to be buried at least one to two metres underground. Again, the hard soil made for heavy digging. We all took turns with picks and shovels to clear the soil and thick grass and weeds. The heat was so overpowering that one of our UN observers had to sit down and put her head between her knees to prevent herself from passing out. We sat her in the shade and urged her to drink as much as possible. It took at least two hours before we heard the unmistakeable dull thud of the shovel hitting the wood of the coffin lids a little over a metre down.

The two coffins lay side by side, and were made of very thick, dark wood. The width of the exhumation site made it difficult to get down into the grave to place ropes under the coffins. As we were deciding how to best proceed, the clouds began rolling in, violent claps of thunder broke overhead and the rain started. Within a few minutes, the grave began to fill with water. Fifteen minutes later, the water was lapping at the tops of the coffins. They became glued into the ground with the mixture of mud and water and there was no way we were going to be able to remove them. After a brief discussion, we decided that the best way to complete the task would be to break open the coffin lids with the shovels and remove the bodies.

We ushered the gathered group away to spare them the trauma of watching us do this. We set to work in the pelting rain and easily removed the coffin lids to reveal the enshrouded bodies. Swiftly but carefully, we lifted out the bodies and placed them into the waiting body bags and onto the back of the tray-truck. It took some effort to make our way back up the small winding pathway from the cemetery to the main road in the downpour. The main road to Dili was treacherous and the dusty winding roads with large potholes had turned into large pools of mud. The roads were very slippery and it took six hours to make the return trip. Once again, I showered, had a quick bite and turned in early.

Our task now was to examine the exhumed bodies. The exhumation itself had gone fairly smoothly and now it was time for me to determine the cause of death. At the mortuary, we opened the body bags from the first exhumation at Ainaro and removed the bodies from the coffins. Both bodies were completely skeletonised. The reports of shooting were confirmed by the telltale damage from the passage of a high-velocity projectile that was immediately obvious in both skulls. One victim had been shot through the right temple and the other through the lower mid-forehead immediately between the eyes. Although the skulls were extensively fragmented, the definitive signs of grooving caused by the bullet passing through bone were apparent.

My examination of the victims from the second exhumation from Ainaro confirmed that the men had indeed been killed by gunshots. The first body I examined showed evidence of decapitation as well as a gunshot wound to the back. I also identified incised wounds on the forearms, which were defence injuries. Furthermore, there was evidence that the left foot had been amputated. This was a horrendous finding, but it fitted with the story of amputation and mutilation that we had heard before the exhumation. The man had suffered at least three separate machete blows to the back of the neck and to the sides of the head, as well as a further tangential chop across the right side of the jaw. The second body also showed evidence of a gunshot to the back. In this case, I was able to recover the oxidised bullet jacketing and the lead core. This ballistic evidence was secured as evidential material and Brian gave it an item number according to protocol. All areas of trauma on the bodies were then identified, separated and photographed individually. Anahi confirmed the age and height of the deceased in a very detailed document that would supplement my own post-mortem.

The body we had exhumed at Cassa was fully skeletonised and, sadly, was incomplete. Many of the bones showed evidence of animal scavenging, which probably explained why some of them were missing. The body had been bound and I removed the ligatures to put them aside as evidence. I noted a large incised injury over the left cheek area, which was the typical sign of a blow from a machete. I thought that the most likely cause of death was that of decapitation. As the skeleton was being cleaned and reassembled, I noted the presence of an old healed fracture to the right lower leg. This finding would prove to be important in the ultimate identification of this victim.

## AITUTO

For the final exhumation for this tour, we pretty much followed the same route from Dili, heading for a village called Aituto, forty-five kilometres due south of Dili, not far from Maubisse. We had passed it on the previous trips, though I hadn't noticed it. We had come to retrieve what was believed to be two bodies buried at the base of a deep ravine. Once again, we were able to identify the grave by the small pile of rocks. A stick had also been driven into the ground to mark the grave. In this case, the locals had heard of a possible killing and clandestine burial and had noticed disturbed soil and a foul odour coming from this spot. They had informed the authorities and, as a result, we were there to begin the formal investigation. We parked the tray-truck at the edge of the road under a large tree and unpacked our picks, shovels and body bags. We walked along a narrow well-trodden path through a wide, sweeping grass plain. On our left was a deep gully filled with palm trees. To our right were towering escarpments partially hidden by clouds. After walking about a kilometre through the chest-high elephant grass, we arrived at the ravine. It was more of a deep gully terminating in a v-shape of fallen soil and boulders.

Sure enough, at the base of this gully, we saw a small pile of rocks and a wooden post. We again took GPS readings and photographed the lay of the land before beginning to dig. Within moments, thirty to forty villagers materialised from the jungle and lined both sides of the ravine. We could feel all eyes watching us intently. As far as we were aware, there was no formal announcement that the exhumation would proceed on this day. The bush telegraph travels exceedingly fast in East Timor. This exhumation took no more than thirty minutes. About a metre or so underground, we found two whitish-grey rice sacks, which had been sewn closed. Each contained the remains of a slain victim. As we started to remove the first of these rice sacks, the traditional wailing of the relatives and villagers began. The mother of one of the deceased was immediately behind my left shoulder and I can still hear her anguished expressions of grief.

I hoped that our efforts were of at least some small comfort to the remaining family and villagers. I was relieved that on this occasion there was no animal sacrifice. After one of the elders had spoken a few words over the gravesite, we placed the remains in the body bags and set off on an alternative route back to the truck. This turned out to be not such a great idea, as we needed to carry every-thing back up a forty-five degree slope. We had to make regular stops to catch our breath, as the temperature and humidity were oppressive. We eventually got to the truck, stored the bodies and equipment in the back and headed back on the now familiar road to the morgue in Dili.

Once we were back at the morgue, we opened the body bags. The two bodies were completely skeletonised. We had been told that the victims were of a similar age. Anahi determined by the pattern of epiphyseal closure of the bones that one was approxi-mately eighteen years of age and the other was probably closer to twenty-three. There were no ligatures or blindfolds on the first victim and no evidence of gunshot, blunt or sharp trauma to the bones. The remains of the second victim also showed no evidence of injury. Disappointingly, we couldn't determine a cause of death, so they were both documented as unascertained deaths. Causes of death such as asphyxia, strangulation or stabbing to the soft tissue could not be excluded and it seemed rather odd that both bodies should fail to show a cause of death in the same scenario. One of the bodies showed evidence of a poorly healed fracture to the left foot, where two of the bones had fused together. This finding proved to be a vital clue in the identification of this indivi-dual as one of the victims had been described as walking with a distinct limp. As usual, we retained biological specimens for DNA analysis.

## ADDITIONAL CASES

Two more fresh cases had materialised while we were in Aituto. The first case was that of a fifty-five year old East Timorese male who had died in custody at the Bercora Prison. In East Timor, a death in custody is a cause of great concern. A meticulous autopsy is required to exclude self-harm, brutality inflicted by other inmates or prison officers and also to identify and exclude natural causes. The investigating unit indicated that at this stage of the examination there was no evidence to suggest that the death was due to anything other than natural causes. The chief prosecutor of Dili gave permission for the autopsy and we began the examination. The body showed no evidence of trauma. The only significant finding was that the heart was moderately enlarged and showed evidence of ventricular thickening almost certainly due to hypertension. I also saw scar tissue within one wall of the heart, which was the hallmark of an old heart attack, and the coronary arteries were significantly narrowed. In all likelihood, this man had probably suffered an uncomplicated heart attack while in custody. This finding was a great relief to the investigating officers, prison officials and no doubt to family members also.

The last case of my rotation concerned a sixteen-year-old local girl, who had apparently dropped dead while eating some rice. I could not see any evidence of trauma or foul play in the external examination. The internal examination showed no abnormalities. As with the toxic crab case, we took tissue specimens fixed in methanol and samples of gastric content, bile, liver and blood for full toxicological analysis. These specimens were forwarded to

Darwin Forensic Science Centre. All results ultimately were returned as normal, so the label of unascertained death had to be accepted once again. The age of the girl made a sudden unexpected death due to natural causes seem unlikely, but all forensic pathologists acknowledge that this can occur. I have occasionally come across such cases at home in Australia. They always remain a great mystery to the pathologist, investigating officers and the family of the deceased. Although it is difficult, I try to be realistic about unexplained deaths. Sometimes, we just do not know what the cause of death is in an otherwise healthy person.

My job here was complete. We reconstructed the two fresh bodies and returned them to their families for burial.

CHOPPER TIME

Now it was time to return the exhumed bodies to their waiting families at Ainaro. The following morning, Brian and I loaded the tray-truck with the body bags and drove to the helicopter airport on the outskirts of the city. A large, white UN Puma helicopter was waiting. Security was strict, and all items such as cigarette lighters and matches were put aside, to be collected on our return. Brian then asked me whether I was okay with everything. I asked him what he meant. He told me that he wasn't coming with me, as he had other things to do that morning. I set off alone with the helicopter pilot for the flight over the trails we had driven over previously. As we took off, I took photographs of Dili and the surrounding suburbs and, later in the flight, of the magnificent, mountainous landscape.

When we reached Ainaro, the helicopter slowly descended over a basketball field. From my vantage point, I could see a multitude of young children running towards the airfield. The helicopter landed, flattening the surrounding grass with clouds of dust. The cool, crisp air was a welcome relief from the mixture of fuel fumes and decomposition in the chopper. We signed the bodies over to the local police officer for repatriation to their waiting families. Within ten minutes we were in the air again, heading back to Dili.

The days had passed quickly this time around. It felt as though I had only been there about a week, but it was actually the fifteenth day of my rotation. That evening was my last night and the team met at a restaurant in an outer suburb of Dili. We had some difficulty finding it, as there were no signs on the outside. This restaurant is known to the locals as 'The Moustache' after the distinguishing feature of its proprietor. This jovial and frequently intoxicated local character specialises in seafood dishes. The prawns came out of the kitchen by the kilogram and the salt and pepper squid was superb. We helped ourselves to drinks from the fridge in the corner of the restaurant and at the end of the night the empties were tallied up. We had a fantastic night, the culmination of a successful rotation. I was grateful for Anahi's outstanding work and took this opportunity to thank her and the others for their great effort. I hoped that I would visit East Timor again, but this would depend on whether any more vacancies became available among the rotating international pathologists. Little did I know that I would be back in July.

## JULY 2002

On 9 July 2002, I was again called upon to go to East Timor to participate in more forensic investigations into war crimes. In what was emerging as a pattern, I was also told that there would probably be further incidental fresh cases, or 'While you are here, Doc' cases to examine. I was beginning to feel like I had become some sort of

body magnet. Whenever I was around, bodies seemed to materialise. I was getting used to the routine now, and it reminded me of
how the local East Timorese usually respond to 'How are things?'
with 'Same, same!'

This time, I flew from Melbourne to Adelaide for a short
stopover before flying to Darwin. I checked into the Carlton Hotel
and, with some apprehension, set off for the UN building to check
the manifest for the flight to Dili the following morning. I had
prepared myself for an all-night fiasco like last time, but, happily,
my name was on the list. I was a bit disappointed that the UN
Hercules C-130 had been decommissioned and all flights to Dili
were by commercial jet. Although this meant being offered all the
usual comforts of commercial flights, I missed the old, uncomfortable Hercules. I really have a soft spot for the large cumbersome
aircraft. I was happy that I got to fly in one again to the Solomon
Islands in January 2004.

Steve Olinder, an Australian Federal Police (AFP) officer met
me at Dili airport. I couldn't mistake him, as his navy blue AFP
issue boiler suit had the word 'Forensic' conspicuously displayed
on the back. His Swedish descent is obvious in his tall, slim build,
light-brown hair and blue eyes. Steve is an extremely affable person,
and we would meet again in subsequent missions in the Solomon
Islands. My immediate concern, as usual, was finding accommodation. Steve and several others were staying at the local power station
that supplies much of East Timor. He invited me to come and have
a look, as he thought there might be one room available.

THE POWER STATION

The power station is situated several blocks behind the morgue,
next to the Comoro River. The large, open factory-like space had

four large marine generators, which worked 24 hours a day. The noise was deafening, and the smell of oil was overpowering. Two hundred metres from the power station were rows of construction huts and behind these stood a ramshackle house that served as the communal kitchen and dining area. A large, well-used barbecue stood on its veranda. The huts were in two rows with a crushed rock pebble courtyard separating them. In the courtyard stood some home-made gym equipment, including dumbbells that had been constructed by fitting a large lump of concrete on each end of a length of iron water pipe. Team members kept in shape using this makeshift gym equipment while doing their rotations. I was offered a small room at one end of the row of containers. The container was very similar to my room at the Dili Lodge Hotel except that there was a small communal toilet and shower block at the end of the row of huts. This was to be a short stay and for ten Australian dollars per night, much less than the cost of the Dili Lodge Hotel, I had everything I needed. I was thankful for the large, powerful air-conditioner above the bedhead. This needed to run day and night to prevent the room turning into an oven. I quickly got used to the continuous roar; it was a small price to pay for a good night's sleep. There was one hitch, though, the intermittent power supply. Throughout the day, the power is shut down at regular intervals so as not to overload the system. When the generators stopped, the silence was stunning and the temperature in the room immediately skyrocketed to the high thirties.

The residents at the power station were the usual collection of UN personnel, as well as some international police officers. There were several other Australians and British and American civilian police officers. As this stay was going to be a short one, I had implored the UN to make the induction as speedy as possible. Thankfully, the process was completed in one day.

SKELETONS

In what was becoming a familiar routine, the following day I was to begin autopsies on several previously exhumed bodies, as well as on some recent cases that had come in before my arrival. After that, I was to be part of two exhumations. One body was buried in a cemetery outside Liquica and the second, an infant, was buried behind the hospital morgue in Dili. Laura, Filomena and Francelino were still there and greeted me with open arms. I looked forward to working with them all again. Sofia Egana had replaced Anahi Ginarte. Vivacious and bubbly, Sofia proved herself to be an exceptional anthropologist and a delight to work with.

The first round of post-mortems were exhumed skeletal remains. The first case was a complete skeleton, which had been unearthed during the construction of a septic tank pit. We examined the remains closely, but were unable to determine for certain how old the remains were. The body was female and of mature age. It was likely that this particular body had nothing whatever to do with the referendum uprising and subsequent atrocities. We were unable to find any evidence of trauma and I had to determine that the cause of death was unascertained.

Suspicious circumstances seemed to surround the next case. This particular body had been found in a well on the Carascalao property next to the Dili Cafe. The Carascalao family featured prominently in the initial referendum uprising and killings. The militia had stormed the home of pro-independence faction leader Manuel Carascalao, killing twelve people who were sheltering there, including his teenage son. The skeletal remains were incomplete and there was no skull present. Once we had cleaned and laid out the bones, the only evidence of trauma we could find was a well-defined vertical cut to the ninth rib on the left side. This single defect was the telltale sign of a deep stab wound, and I determined that the cause of death was stabbing. Without the skull, we were unable to speculate on whether there could also have been blunt force and hacking wounds such as we had seen in the first and second missions.

The third examination of the day was another skeletonised body, which had been found at Alas. This body showed the horrendous injuries that I had become familiar with during the examinations on the victims of the Passabe massacre. The most significant was a deep depressed fracture in the skull, caused by a blow to the head. There was also an oblique-oriented incised cut through the right side of the jaw in keeping with the cutting action of a machete. This was typical of an East Timorese post-referendum killing.

In all cases, the bones were relatively clean and required minimal effort to process. As usual, Sofia and I put together the documentation and photographs of the bones and sites of injury for the forensic record.

The following day, we performed a further examination on a fully skeletonised body that had been found near the Dili airport in an area called Canada Camp. This body showed such severe degradation of virtually all of the bones that I concluded the remains were more likely to be of archaeological than forensic interest. Sofia and I both agreed that the death of the individual predated the times of the recent conflict. While we were able to designate the age, height and sex of the deceased, we could not detect any areas of significant trauma. Once again, I had to give an unascertained cause of death.

MORE CASES

The first case the following day was a partial torso in a state of advanced decomposition. The body had been found above ground in a wet environment at Emera. According to local knowledge, this person had been the victim of a machete attack. We removed the cut-off khaki shorts and the tattered remnants of a white polo-shirt. The degree of decomposition was extensive and it appeared that this victim had been subjected to extensive post-mortem animal scavenging and feeding. The mandible was absent, as was much of the cervical and thoracic vertebrae, almost all of the ribs, the left arm and the lower right leg. The lower limbs, particularly the bone shafts of the femur and fibula, showed the gnawed edges typical of the chewing of scavenging animals. I noted a small five-millimetre perforation through the skull, but I determined that this was caused by the teeth of a marauding animal, rather than a gunshot wound. Luckily, the lower right side of the ribcage remained intact. After we cleaned this area, we found several deep incised wounds directly in line with one another on the eighth, ninth and tenth ribs. This was proof of stabbing to this area, and I designated this as the cause of death in this individual.

That afternoon, we were asked to examine the fresh body of a woman who had been found hanging by the neck. The local police regarded this case as highly suspicious, as the suspension point of the ligature was above the bed and the deceased had been found on the bed in a semi-crouched position. In almost all cases of hanging, the individual is either fully suspended from the ground, or at least the feet are touching the ground with the knees flexed. This case required a complete and thorough examination in the traditional style as performed back home and I needed a complete set of surgical instruments. The instruments were brought out of the storeroom. To my horror, many were missing. The box contained only a few pairs of extremely blunt scissors and long-bladed knives, toothed forceps and a scalpel. The scissors and knives were so blunt that they were completely useless for post-mortem work and there was no oilstone to sharpen them. To demonstrate how useless they were, I rolled up my sleeve and rubbed the sharp edge of the knife along my forearm. The others recoiled in horror, but there was no mark left on my arm at all. I wondered how I was going to perform a full autopsy on a recently dead victim with only a pair of forceps and a scalpel. Steve saved the day by producing a pair of nail scissors from his personal kit. I was a bit dubious about how effective they would be, but they were our best option at this point. I warned him that he might not want them back after I had finished. This was the first case in my professional career where I had been required to examine a complete and intact body with a scalpel and pair of nail scissors. Still, it was better than a pair of forceps and a blunt knife.

The autopsy was not easy. Examining a large organ such as the liver with a small thirty millimetre knife was heavy going. But we persisted and were able to determine that this death appeared to be a suicide rather than a suspicious death. I could find no evidence of defence injuries on the young woman and there was no evidence of a struggle. I explained that this case almost certainly fitted into the minority of hangings where the body is in an unusual position, but that it did not necessarily mean other people had been involved.

Laura and Filomena managed to find additional instruments to assist in any later fresh cases so that this situation would not occur again. From now on, I would always bring my own instruments. My personal instrument case now weighs approximately fifteen kilograms and contains everything necessary to conduct autopsies in all circumstances of death. It also contains anthropological instruments, pro-formas, skeletal maps, anthropology charts and plenty of disposable post-mortem gloves. I want to make sure I don't get caught out like that again.

The evenings spent at the power station were most pleasant. As the sun set, the temperature dropped to the middle to low twenties, though the humidity remained high. We would often have a barbecue on the landing of the house, or perhaps visit one of the local restaurants. The number of restaurants and nightclubs in Dili had blossomed since my first visit in early 2000. Many of the restaurants were quite sophisticated, with an extensive range of meals and a formidable wine list. Nightclubs and restaurants had appeared along the coast road leading to the Jesus statue. On some evenings we had difficulty finding a parking spot. I was uncomfortable about the complete absence of East Timorese in these popular gathering spots. The parking area was completely filled with shiny new UN vehicles carrying their heavily cashed-up personnel. I think this display of wealth and privilege contributed to the many unprovoked attacks on international staff by roaming local gangs. The streets were decidedly unsafe and we were advised to only go out in twos or threes.

The following morning before breakfast, Steve and I scaled the two large, cylindrical fuel tanks with spiral ladders behind our huts. When we reached the top, we took in the panoramic views of the heavily foliaged hills behind the mortuary. Behind this was a tall watchtower, but its steps didn't look very sturdy, so we didn't try climbing it. Breakfast was usually just a cup of coffee and some cereal. I didn't mind, as I was never much of a breakfast person. After breakfast we set off again for the mortuary where two more cases awaited our attention. These two cases proved to be extremely tragic. This mission seemed to be more about contemporary fresh cases than the militia killings.

The first case was that of an extremely emaciated East Timorese male about thirty or thirty-five years of age. Although we could not weigh the body, we agreed that he weighed no more than thirty-five kilograms. Our information was that this man suffered from a mental illness, possibly schizophrenia. It was alleged that he had been taken into the jungle by his family, tied to a log and left to die. I was told that in the villages of East Timor, those with mental illness are frequently treated in this way. The external examination disclosed sunken eye globes, prominent cheeks and marked wasting of muscles of the upper and lower limbs. His ribs were prominent and there was virtually no abdominal fat to be seen. The internal examination showed evidence of pneumonia involving the right and left upper lobes of his lung, but in all other respects the examination was normal. This poor man had died as a result of exposure, dehydration and, subsequently, pneumonia.

The second case of the day was that of a two-year-old child, who was thought to have died of malaria. Malaria, among other tropical diseases, is endemic in East Timor, so I wasn't sure why this case needed forensic examination. Steve then told me that the child had allegedly been given an injection of anti-malarial medication by an unauthorised and unqualified person after the family had sought help from a local witchdoctor. The death was a notifiable one because the medication had been given by an unauthorised person. The child's body had been in the refrigerator for several days and was already showing the early stages of decomposition. In all other respects, the child appeared well nourished and showed no evidence of maltreatment. The internal examination was more or less normal, with the only relevant finding being a shrunken thymus gland, testimony to some kind of stress, possibly induced by infection. There was no evidence of skull fracture or haemorrhage around the brain, which would indicate trauma. This case was flagged as unascertained pending results of toxicology and histology. As in previous problematic cases in fresh bodies, appropriate specimens were retained and forwarded to Australia for full testing. Months later, I received the toxicology report indicating that anti-malarial medications were detected. The level of

Chloroquine appeared elevated, but did not fall into the lethal range. I concluded that, in all probability, this young child had died of malaria and not as a direct result of the administration of the medication.

After a brief lunchbreak, I was then asked to examine some skeletal remains that had been unearthed by a local farmer near a beachfront in the village of Los Palos. It was the opinion of the investigating officers that the skeletal remains may have dated back to the Second World War. There had been fierce fighting in East Timor and the Solomon Islands during the Second World War and no one knew how many bodies were lying undetected beneath beach sand or dense jungle. These particular bodies had been uncovered during construction or farming activities.

The body bag contained the largely degraded and brittle skeletons of two adults. Sofia and I both thought that it was possible that these bodies could indeed date back to the Second World War. Both were male and in their late teens, certainly the demographic that would be expected in war casualties. One of the bodies showed two conspicuous deep incised defects to the breastbone, which could conceivably have been caused by a bayonet. The other body showed a gaping incised defect through the right side of the cranium, which again may have been caused by a bayonet or similar weapon. This body in particular also showed rather prominent green staining over the pelvic bones and the left wrist. As we separated the bones, we found a metallic buckle. We cleaned the buckle to see if there were any distinguishing marks to help date the victim. The buckle was attached to the remnant of a canvas belt and appeared to be military. The consensus, including the opinion of some members of the SCIU who had military interests, was that this body was probably a Japanese soldier who had been killed in the Second World War, though Sofia couldn't determine the race definitively from studying the skull. We set aside the remains and the appropriate war graves authorities were notified.

We took a rest day the following day and Steve took me to the tais open-air market, a pleasant drive inland from the coast roads. The market sells the usual tourist items of pottery, jewellery, ceremonial swords, carved wooden figures and, of course, the ubiquitous tais. The tais is generally a long, rectangular highly coloured and decorative piece of fabric. It is often given as a gift and is used to decorate the home and in ceremonies to honour the living and dead. I bought quite a few of these beautiful pieces of cloth as souvenirs for people back home. I also bought a very appealing terracotta tea set. Steve found a cardboard box and yards of bubble wrap and I was able to safely take it home in my hand luggage. These beautiful items now decorate my home.

EXHUMATIONS

The remainder of the mission involved two further exhumations and autopsies. The first exhumation was that of a young twelve-year-old East Timorese male who had died in suspicious circumstances. The child had been buried in a legitimate cemetery on the outskirts of Liquica. Steve and I knew Liquica well and it was only a forty-minute drive away. We thought we could get there, exhume the body and be back in time to perform the autopsy by that afternoon. We were wrong, again. Rather than taking the 4WD tray-truck on this occasion, we were given a small, white minibus. Steve and I and several other civilian police officers boarded the minibus on the road to Liquica. We stopped off at the local police station to show our authorisation papers and were told that the cemetery was not within the immediate township, but ten to fifteen kilometres further along the coast road and inland.

The second leg of this trip took about one and a half hours through the most difficult terrain, far worse than on the previous mission in the south of the island. The small, winding dirt road up the mountain was little more than a goat track, with no room to turn around if we needed to. I was glad that I wasn't driving. The minibus was bogged several times in the large, dust-filled cavities in the road, and often the road was almost too narrow for the wheels. We all looked nervously at the steep descent to our right as parts of the road crumbled underneath us. We finally reached the village, to our great relief, and were greeted by a multitude of villagers as they rushed out of their huts with the familiar 'Hello mister!' I've never been so relieved to reach a destination.

We walked the short distance to the cemetery in the sweltering heat. Already, all the team members were sweating profusely. We began digging once we had photographed the little grave. The soil was red-orange in colour and had been baked hard in the glaring sun of the dry season. It took us over an hour to reach the coffin lid. We took further photographs at this point and then placed the small coffin into a body bag and onto the minibus and set off back to Dili. As we had lost so much time that day, we decided to defer the examination until the following morning.

The next morning, we retrieved the little coffin from the refrigerator and photographed it again before we opened it. Two army dentists had asked to view the autopsy and the team leader had granted permission. Once the lid was opened, the body of a well-nourished twelve-year-old child in the early stages of decomposition was revealed. The child was fully clothed and several items of clothing had also been placed on top of the body. The story was that the child had possibly died as the result of a head injury after being struck on the right side of the head by a knife, allegedly thrown by his mother. The child had lapsed into unconsciousness and had been rushed to hospital and given urgent neurosurgery to evacuate a presumed blood clot surrounding the brain. There were no CAT-scan facilities in East Timor, so we presumed that the neurosurgeon had performed an exploratory operation. There was a surgical dressing on the head of the child and, beneath this, a sutured, curved incision measuring eighty-eight millimetres over the apex of his shaved scalp.

The internal examination showed extensive haemorrhage into the muscles of the right temple and a small fracture through the base of the left side of the skull. Further examination revealed some patchy bruising over both left and right upper arms, which were in keeping with gripping or shaking. There was no significant area of haemorrhage around the brain, but the brain did appear to be markedly tense and swollen. This condition is called cerebral oedema, which, if left unchecked, ultimately leads to death. The child had also developed broncho-pneumonia during his short survival period. The immediate cause of death was therefore unclear. It could have been the blunt trauma, a vigorous shaking or a complication of his surgery. We may never know.

I also found several large tapeworms about fifteen to eighteen centimetres long present in the body. Parasites such as this are endemic in East Timor. We preserved one of these tapeworms in a jar of formalin and set it aside. Perhaps it would be the beginning of a pathology museum at the mortuary. The forensic technicians reconstructed the body and it was released to the family for burial.

Later that evening, the two army dentists invited us to join the meal at the army hospital base that had been set up immediately across the road from the mortuary. I was shown the rather sophisticated operating theatre within the main building and the x-ray facilities housed outside in large inflated tents. The mess tent was behind the main building and a basic but sumptuous meal was provided, which Steve and I ate with great relish.

THIS ONE'S ON ME

The last case of the mission was to be performed the following day. An infant had been buried in an unmarked grave behind the mortuary of the local hospital in Dili. This young baby had apparently been born in the jungle to an unwed mother. The allegation was that the child had been placed behind a tree and then a rock weighing about five kilograms had been placed on top of its chest. The infant had apparently died of asphyxia. There were several pressing forensic questions to be answered. Had the child been born alive? Could it have survived unaided and unassisted? The child had been found by another villager and immediately taken to hospital, where it had survived for a time. It had then allegedly developed septicaemia and infection and had died of complications. There had been questions raised about the medical management of this small baby.

Steve and I packed some shovels and trowels and headed off to the gravesite at the back of the hospital. When we arrived, we were shown a grassy area punctuated by numerous small, white rocks, each marking the grave of a baby. None of the graves had markers as such, but a member of the hospital management showed us the exact place to dig. Within half an hour, we reached a small bundle and carefully removed it from the ground. The baby had been wrapped in several sheets and was fully dressed. The little bundle had been buried about two months previously. Back at the mortuary, after taking preliminary photographs, we unwrapped the small body. We were disappointed to find that there was nothing more than a collection of tiny bones remaining. The state of decomposition was such that all soft tissues had been lost, obliterating any chance of answering the pivotal questions of survival after birth, the immediate cause of death and the medical management. The examination took no more than ten minutes and I apologetically told Steve that I had no way of providing answers to these important questions. As I was paid on a contractual basis per body, I told Steve that there would be no need to include the examination of this body in the fee I was to be paid. This one was on me.

After the examination, I was given the statements of the various people involved in this case. The opinion of the treating physicians at the local hospital was that the child had survived for approximately thirteen days, and it was deemed to be a low birthweight though full-term baby. The child had marked noisy breathing and might have been born with a tracheal abnormality. There were problems during intubation that substantiated this possibility. The child had then developed a high fever and, in spite of aggressive treatment with antibiotics, had died of presumed septicaemia. I was unable to advance on this report any further, but after reading the medical notes, I concluded that everything that could have been done had in fact been done for this small baby. I was saddened by the treatment of the mentally ill and unwanted children in East Timor. Steve told me of anecdotal cases where unwanted children were disposed of in a similar harsh and uncaring fashion. Many unwanted pregnancies in East Timor are attributed to incest rather than birth out of wedlock. It was a sad end to a busy day.

It was now my final night in East Timor and, in what was something of a tradition, the team went out to one of the local restaurants for a last meal. I had a feeling that this could be my last trip to East Timor. There were rumours that the SCIU would be scaled down and the mortuary decommissioned, with all autopsies being performed at the local hospital. It was also becoming very unlikely that all the bodies in and around the area would be exhumed purely for the purpose of identification and the cause of death. From the prosecutor's point of view, a significant number of bodies had been exhumed and examined over the previous two years and the major players in these atrocities had been charged.

I had found this last mission rather taxing and surprising. As the year 2002 progressed, the phone was silent from East Timor and it seemed that the remainder of the year might go by without any overseas action. This changed dramatically in December of that year.

# SIX

# EAST TIMOR
## DECEMBER 2002

### DILI SHOOTOUT

My last mission to East Timor was in December 2002, in response to a mass riot in Dili on 4 December. It was the worst violence in the capital since Indonesian troops and their militia proxies withdrew in 1999. Xanana Gusmao had been elected President in May of that year, but there were still incidents demonstrating an underlying unrest between some locals and police and hostility towards the foreign presence. Just before this uprising, there had been an incident between police and locals in the district of Baucau situated north-east of Dili, known for violent disturbances between local factions. Local and international police arrived at a village to investigate a complaint that some members of the village were setting up roadblocks and then demanding money from travellers before they would let them pass. An argument broke out between the police and the locals and a Timorese police officer was wounded with a machete. During the subsequent scuffle, one of the villagers involved was shot and wounded by police. In protest, a local leader organised a demonstration, drawing a great crowd. The demonstrators became violent as they marched towards the local police headquarters. The police, under pressure from the abuse and threats of the angry crowd, fired shots and in the ensuing shoot-out a young man, Calsitro Soares, was killed.

A few days later, on 4 December, a demonstration was arranged in Dili following the detention of a student during an earlier bout of civil unrest. Radical forces agitated and inflamed the student demonstration, which escalated into a rampage of violence and bloodshed. Tensions had been growing between the impoverished locals and the United Nations (UN) staff and foreign businesses during the second half of 2002, and there was a distinct anti-UN feeling. There had been many unprovoked attacks on international civilian personnel, including rocks being thrown at UN vehicles, caused by a general feeling of frustration and hostility as the impoverished local population watched the affluent internationals driving new vehicles and spending their American dollars. These tensions now erupted as the protesters turned to torching the houses, businesses and vehicles of westerners. During the uprising, the Hello Mister supermarket, owned by an Australian and selling goods too expensive for locals to buy, was vandalised. A mosque was burnt, parliament buildings and the residence of the Prime Minister, Mari Alkatiri, were vandalised and burnt in a frenzy of destruction. Although violence was mainly directed at buildings and property, Australian Federal Police (AFP) officers, UN workers and local police were also the target of attacks. Armed UN troops and police guarded buildings and fired warning shots at protesters in an attempt to disperse the demonstrators and protect the estimated thirteen hundred Australians and other foreigners who were under siege in their homes and offices.

President Xanana Gusmao went to the scene of the riots in an unsuccessful attempt to restore order. After several days, the violence gradually subsided. Fifteen people had been shot, two had been killed and many others injured. Police arrested eighty people and the government formed a task force to identify those responsible for the rioting, arson and looting, and vowed to punish the guilty. It was feared that the violence could have been due to the reappearance of the Indonesian militia. This posed a serious threat to the stability of the country and undermined the recent efforts towards reconciliation as well as drawing international condemnation. Even worse, there were accusations that the shots were fired by the UN or other security forces and the media ran prominent pictures of police firing into the crowds. These two deaths were declared to be the latest in a series of police shootings and UN headquarters demanded to know who was responsible for the killings. It was vital that the President find the perpetrators and bring them to justice and thereby restore order in the country.

## URGENT CALL FROM DILI

I heard about this latest development as I was driving along the Monash freeway on my way to work at the Victorian Institute of Forensic Medicine (VIFM). The early morning news was full of the Dili uprising. I wondered whether this latest disturbing incident would require the services of an international pathologist. There would probably be forensic staff in Dili at this time, so it was unlikely that I would be called to help.

The VIFM holds a weekly clinico-pathological meeting where we describe difficult or interesting cases. All staff are invited to attend. I was already seated in the auditorium when Professor Stephen Cordner, the director of the Institute, took his usual place in the centre-front row. He asked me whether I had had any phone calls from Dili and I replied in the negative. The meeting proceeded as usual and broke up an hour later. At ten o'clock, an urgent call came for me from Dili. Nikolai, a UN worker, asked me whether I was available to fly to Dili the following day to examine the slain victims of the shooting. I was granted leave from the Institute and arrangements were immediately made so that I was scheduled to fly out at ten thirty the next morning. Late that night at home, I had a further call. Nikolai had been in direct communication with the President of East Timor, Xanana Gusmao, and I could tell by the tone in his voice that he was under considerable pressure to get me into Dili as soon as possible. I told him that I would be flying out the following morning. Nikolai told me that the President had said, 'I want Dodd. Get him on the next plane, no matter what the cost.' I told him that if he could organise an earlier flight, I would be on it. Approximately half an hour later, I was booked on a flight for ten past seven the following morning.

The evening news reported further on the extent of the uprising. The Australian embassy had been sandbagged and was heavily guarded. There was talk of rapidly withdrawing all international personnel from the capital. I watched the graphic footage of people running in terror, shots being fired and bodies lying on the ground. For the first time since the beginning of 2000, I had genuine concerns for my personal safety. My wife, Martine, was doubly concerned. But I knew from past experience that I would be heavily guarded and protected during my three-day stay. During previous missions, heavily armed civilian police and private security were nearby at all times, at the mortuary, during the exhumation process and during visits to the UN compound. I reassured Martine that I would be looked after and that there should be no real concern about my safety.

There was one snag that could delay my journey. Nikolai told me that my time of arrival in Darwin would be very close to the time of departure of the flight to Dili and there was a chance that I might miss the connection. This would mean an overnight stay in Darwin while I waited for the next connecting flight. To prevent this, I was told that the President himself had arranged for the plane to remain on the tarmac until my arrival. Engine trouble or awaiting new supplies would be the excuse given for any delay.

After an uneventful flight to Darwin, a UN representative met me at the airport and hurriedly arranged the collection of my baggage and payment of departure tax. I was then ushered to the international departure lounge on the first floor. It seemed that as soon as I arrived in the lounge everyone was moved out onto the tarmac to board the small jet aircraft. As I waited in line to board the aircraft, I met an AFP officer named Justine Adamek. Justine was at that time based in Canberra and had received her papers to go to East Timor for a tour of duty. We struck up an immediate friendship. Justine is vibrant, chatty and very friendly. During the flight we exchanged travellers' tales. She was very interested in my previous experiences in East Timor and I was surprised to learn that she had also been in Kosova around the same time as me in 2000. Justine had been based in Orahovac and so our paths had not crossed. She was flying to Dili to act as scene-of-crime officer for the Special Crimes Investigation Unit (SCIU), so we would be working closely together over the following three days. Many of our fellow passengers were flying to Dili for the first time; others were seasoned travellers to this area and were going back for a second or third mission.

The plane touched down at Dili airport, which had changed little since my last visit in July. As I descended the mobile gantry, I was met by Siri Frigaard, the deputy chief prosecutor for the UN in

East Timor, and a Canadian civilian police officer. Siri led us directly to the executive lounge. This sounded impressive and as I hadn't yet eaten, I imagined sitting down for a coffee and perhaps something to eat. But this was not to be. Siri took my passport from me and had it processed immediately. She was able to circumvent the usual customs and immigration process, thereby saving us at least an hour.

## THE VICTIMS

We proceeded directly to the morgue at the agricultural college at Comoro. I was to begin immediately. I queried the need for such urgency. Siri explained that the grieving families of the slain victims had been promised that the bodies would be returned that evening by helicopter. She told me I would have to work fast as the weather was closing in and could cause difficulties for the helicopter in taking off on time. We hoped to lift off at eight o'clock. Looking at the sky over the hills, I saw menacing, dark clouds accumulating as we spoke. I would indeed have to work fast to complete the autopsies on time. Happily, my co-workers Laura, Filomena and Francelino were all still working at the mortuary and greeted me warmly. It seemed like only yesterday that I had left the mortuary, rather than four and a half months ago. Little had changed, except that on this occasion there was a good supply of post-mortem instruments.

President Gusmao's immediate concern was to find out who had fired the shots that had killed the young men who now lay before me in body bags. Was it a militia faction, or one of the civilian police officers, or a private security agent? The consequences of these findings would have extreme ramifications. If we found that the first victim had been shot by a UN police officer or a security agent, the finding could precipitate another bout of massive civil unrest that could seriously undermine efforts to rebuild the shattered country. If we found that the bullet had been fired by a militia agent using a military style, high-velocity weapon, it could avert further uprisings.

Because of the gravity of the situation, both bodies had been x-rayed at the hospital across the road before I arrived. I held the x-rays up to the light of the window to examine them. I could see no evidence of retained projectiles or bullet jacketing. The bullet had passed cleanly through the body without leaving a trace of metallic residue within the tissues. I knew that this was the hallmark of a high-velocity discharge and certainly not that of a handgun. This preliminary finding was heartening.

After photographs were taken of the first slain victim, I began the autopsy. The deceased man was aged twenty and had been wrapped in sheets inside the body bag. He was otherwise naked. There was no evidence of medical intervention. I traced the trajectory of the projectile and established the extent of the internal trauma. The bullet had passed through the left arm, exited at the armpit and re-entered the upper left chest. The bullet had then exited through his upper right chest and directly through the right arm. In forensic parlance, this is a through-and-through shot; the fact that the bullet had traversed the greatest dimension of the body and had left no shrapnel confirmed my initial impression that this was the result of a high-velocity discharge from a military weapon. The bullet had missed his heart by inches, but had torn apart the large vessel arising from the heart and caused instantaneous and lethal blood loss. This victim had died instantly. There was no physical evidence of the bullet, so I documented the injuries and wrote up my conclusion about the type of weapon most likely to be the cause of these injuries.

After a quick coffee break, we began the second post-mortem examination. This second case was that of a death in custody. An eighteen-year-old East Timorese man was called to halt by security officers when he was seen fleeing on a bicycle. He had ignored the command several times and was subsequently shot by an officer with a pistol. The young man was rushed to hospital, but had died on the operating table. AFP officer Phil Turner took external photographs as we began the external examination. Upon opening the body bag, we could see the heavily blood-soaked absorbent surgical dressings, which concealed the lower half of the abdominal wall. As I worked on the external examination, I saw that the bullet had passed through the victim's right buttock and had exited through the lower right pelvic area. In doing so, the bullet had shattered the pelvic bone and had ruptured many large, deep blood vessels. These injuries were caused by a single gunshot injury and, as a result, the young man had bled to death. Again, the bullet had passed completely through the body, so we found no evidential material.

As I conducted the autopsy, I could hear a large, angry and agitated crowd gathering outside the mortuary building. Because this was a police shooting, it was possible that the situation could turn violent. I tried to ignore the distraction as I worked through the autopsy as swiftly as possible. On several occasions during the procedure, a head would appear around the corner of the autopsy room to ask how long it would be before the body could be released. As the crowd outside grew rowdier, I emphasised the urgency of the task to Filomena and Laura, who reconstructed the body in record time. Everything was ready for the helicopter to take off forty-five minutes later, just as the weather was closing in. The body of this young man was released and flown home to the waiting family as promised. It was with some relief that I sat down to prepare the hand-written interim report.

After the day's work was complete, I asked Justine if she had any ideas about where I could stay for the night. She was billeted at the power station and I told her that I had fond memories of my stay there earlier in the year. I would be more than happy to stay there again if there was a room available. After cleaning the mortuary and setting aside the instruments, we set off in the 4WD to the power station to see what was available. All the construction huts were occupied, although there was a small bed out the back of the main building, tucked in among the supplies of food and camping gear. This would suit me fine for two nights. It was certainly preferable to the *Hotel Olympia*.

The group at the power station consisted of the usual UN personnel and federal police officers from Canberra. There was also a colourful, verbose Texan, an Irish woman and a British civilian police officer. The meal was a simple one, and after a few drinks and a cup of coffee, I retired early to my bed. I was awoken early the next morning by the sound of roosters crowing. Justine told me that another case had been admitted to the mortuary for immediate attention.

## THE LADY ON THE BEACH

There were many 'While you are here, Doc' cases during my missions to East Timor. On this occasion, the body of a mutilated and partially burnt female had been found on a beachfront. When we opened the body bag, it gave off a strong smell of kerosene or diesel fuel. The body was a woman of unknown age and identity. Justine acted as scene-of-crime officer and took the post-mortem photographs. The body revealed extensive post-mortem animal feeding activity. Much of the soft tissues of the chest, abdominal wall, pelvis and limbs had been taken by marauding pigs, which are known to frequent the beaches of Dili.

After a full autopsy, I was unable to identify any evidence of inflicted trauma, other than the obvious areas of burning to the outside of her body. I meticulously examined the delicate neck structures, but this did not reveal any zones of bruising or fracture. There was no trauma to the head, no bruising or lacerations. I did note that the mucous membrane of the back of the throat and the upper part of the trachea were intensely inflamed. I came to the conclusion that the woman had died as a result of inhalation of super-heated gas and perhaps a small amount of smoke as a result of the fire. I was to learn from Justine months later that this case was fully investigated and concluded. Justine, a federal police officer, was later to write up her experiences in East Timor in the Australian Police publication *Platypus* (79, June 2003 4–11). I quote from her article:

> The body position referred to as pugilistic with flexed arms, hands and feet, and its blackened colour, were consistent with the remains having been burnt. Not much of her body was intact. Only her long, black hair, matted with sand and seaweed, half of her face, her teeth and one of her feet remained whole. Certainly not enough for a visual identification. Because of the public location and other factors, it was obvious the woman's body had been only recently dumped. It was also evident her death or the burning of the remains had not occurred where the body was found.
>
> The lack of computerised or centralised reporting meant that trying to establish whether any person had recently been reported missing was a difficult task. By the time the post-mortem examination had been conducted three days later, police were no closer to determining the identity of the deceased.
>
> The post-mortem examination returned a probable cause of death—a conclusion made difficult by the damage caused by the foraging animals and the burning. Important clues included the existence of pink toenail paint still evident on an intact big toe, and a rather prominent chip in one front tooth. She had a strong odour

of flammable liquid in her hair. She was a very slight woman, she looked very young and at first, we believed her to be a juvenile.

Over the next few days, snippets of information came to light, which eventually led police to establish the identity of the woman, in her mid twenties, estranged from her husband. It transpired the couple had a very volatile relationship, caused, in part, by her inability to bear children.

On the evening of December 3, the man had returned home and an argument developed over the woman's failure to prepare the evening meal. The man choked the woman until she passed out. Believing her dead, he went about trying to find the means to dispose of her body. He tried to dig a hole in the back yard of their residence, however, he did not have the proper tools and soon gave up. He dragged her into the yard, doused her with flammable liquid, believed to be kerosene, and lit it. The pathologist believed she was still alive, although unconscious, at the time she was burnt. Her burning was likely to have been the cause of death.

The man then covered her body in rice sacks, and hailed a taxi. He placed the body inside the sacks in the boot of the taxi, and later dumped her body at the beach where it was located. He told police he had placed her into the water, but the shallow bay and the ebbing tide meant that as the water receded, the body remained.

Tragically, as is the culture with many Timorese people, it seemed this man became instantly and fatally violent over a seemingly mundane issue. When confronted by police he freely confessed his actions.

The circumstances of this case were bizarre, especially the fact that the man had taken his wife's body in a taxi to dump it. Several potential family members had gathered at the mortuary to identify her. The body bag was brought into the mortuary. To spare the family the tragedy of viewing her mutilated and burnt body, only her head and neck were exposed. The group immediately identified her by her chipped front tooth.

## A MEETING WITH THE PRESIDENT

I'd just changed out of my scrubs at the conclusion of this sad case, when my mobile phone rang. Siri was on the line and told me that President Xanana Gusmao wanted to see me immediately about the results of the gunshot victims. She told me that this was highly unusual, as the President never saw anyone on a Sunday, which was his designated family day. I told her that I was not dressed appropriately for a Presidential visit, as I had just come from the mortuary. She said, 'It doesn't matter—just be there!' Within twenty minutes, a UN vehicle had arrived at the mortuary to take me to the President's compound. I thought we would take the coast road to Government House on Dili Harbour. Instead, the vehicle left the main road and turned left towards a whitewashed, partially burnt-out building that was heavily guarded. After a five-minute wait in the anteroom, I was ushered into the President's office by one of his aides. The President was dressed in a pair of jeans and white t-shirt. His casual dress and endearing manner immediately set me at ease. He shook my hand and offered me a seat in his office. Within moments, a cup of wonderful black, East Timorese coffee had materialised.

The President immediately offered his thanks not only for completing the most recent cases, but also for my previous work in the country. He was fully aware of my role in the early post-referendum days. I was certainly humbled by his acknowledgement of my efforts. He wanted to know first-hand the findings of the autopsies of the two victims of the recent uprising. I was able to reassure him, to the best of my ability, that the first victim had died as a result of a high-velocity gunshot wound. The nature of the gunshot was entirely consistent with a high-velocity weapon and not the hand-held pistol that would have been carried by a UN or security staff member. He responded by saying, 'Thank God for this, you have probably averted another civil war.' I wasn't sure that that was entirely the case, but I was glad to be able to present this finding. I went on to describe the interpretation of the wounds of the second victim. He acknowledged that this was a sad incident, but not unexpected in an aftermath of this magnitude.

We spent about ten minutes discussing the cases, and after that, the President freely discussed his vision for this fledgling nation. I was impressed by his genuine concern for the future of East Timor. As I sensed the conversation was drawing to an end, I respectfully asked him whether I could have his ear for another ten minutes or so. I dearly wanted to raise the case of the toxic crab with him. I asked him whether he had actually received the report regarding the victim who had consumed the crab. He had not heard of it, so I outlined in some detail how the events had unfolded and my interpretation of the case. I stressed to him that many people could well have died in the past and may do so in the future unless a public awareness campaign was instigated. He agreed that this was a public safety issue and that he would pass it on to the relevant minister. I was greatly reassured by this and thanked him for his time. I then asked him whether it would be possible to have a photograph taken with him as a memento of this last and most significant mission. The President gracefully assented and as we shook hands his secretary took two photographs with my camera. I hoped that they would turn out, which they did, if slightly out of focus. This photo now sits above my desk in my office at the VIFM. It was a memorable occasion and one that I look back on with pride.

Siri was waiting for me outside and drove me back to the power station. Moments later, my mobile phone rang again. This time, it was Professor Stephen Cordner. He had phoned to see how things had progressed and I told him with great satisfaction that I had concluded the two cases, as well as a third homicide case. I told him that I had been summoned to the President's compound where I had explained my findings in person and that the President had listened to my concerns for public safety following the findings of the crab case. He suggested that if at all possible, I should go to the hospital to examine all the surviving victims of the Dili shootout.

## THE SURVIVORS

I had the rest of the afternoon free, so I got a lift to the hospital and located Glen Guest, the surgeon responsible for the management of the gunshot victims. Glen is a general surgeon from St Vincent's hospital in Melbourne and was working in East Timor in a voluntary capacity. He had been very much involved with the victims of the shootings. As the casualties were admitted, he had capably tended to them and had also taken detailed photographs of all the wounds. I could only imagine the chaos in the hospital when the flood of victims arrived at the accident and emergency department. It would have resembled a casualty clearing station during a time of war. I told him that gunshot wounds were one of my areas of particular interest and he offered to take me to his small house behind the hospital to show me the images. As he was on his honeymoon at the time, I also met his new wife and spent an hour or so with them both looking at the photos and chatting about my previous work in East Timor and Kosova.

Glen and I then went to the surgical ward of the hospital. Over the following hour, he allowed me to examine all of the thirteen surviving victims lying in their hospital beds. To my surprise, the entry and exit wounds of many of these survivors had not been sutured, but had been left to drain naturally. Many of these victims had suffered very serious injuries, while others had only superficial wounds. The bullet entry wounds ranged from shots to the upper chest, back, pelvic and buttock areas and, in the minority of cases, to the upper and lower limbs. Glen told me that there was a further gunshot victim who had not presented himself at the hospital. Many of the injuries were severe, particularly those affecting the chest and abdominal walls. I spoke again with Glen on the phone in early 2005 and he told me that all of the victims had survived and were doing well. The survival rate, I am sure, was largely due to Glen's surgical prowess.

The activities at the mortuary that morning, the discussion with President Gusmao that followed, and the ward round in the evening, had made it a very full day. That night, as was customary, the group went out to one of the many local restaurants that had sprung up in Dili for a farewell dinner. We all dined heartily on an excellent Chinese meal and then returned to the power station for a good night's sleep. I was booked on an early morning flight back to Darwin and Melbourne. On the plane back home, I wondered when the next call from Timor would come.

Two and a half years have now passed. I have spoken to several UN workers since my last mission, and sadly, the feeling was that the SCIU would be downscaled and the mortuary closed. The momentum had slowed finally and there were sufficient cases on record for the purposes of prosecution. In spite of my many missions to East Timor, and the many cases I have examined, I have yet to receive a call to return to give evidence. I am also still yet to be convinced that a public awareness campaign on the dangers of toxic crabs was ever put in place.

# SEVEN

# SOLOMON ISLANDS
## SEPTEMBER 2003 AND OCTOBER 2003

## SOLOMON ISLANDS

The Solomon Islands are a scattered archipelago of approximately a thousand islands in the South Pacific Ocean just east of Papua New Guinea and northeast of Cape York on the northern tip of Australia. The Solomon Islands were part of the British Western Pacific Territories until July 1971. The islands were occupied by the Japanese during the Second World War from May 1942 to February 1943 and were the scene of more than a dozen of the Pacific war's lengthiest and most bitterly fought naval battles between the US and Japan. Sea and aircraft wreckage as well as tanks and cannon still litter the jungle landscape and the coastal waters.

The Solomon Islands achieved self-government in January 1976, followed by independence from the British on 7 July 1978. The first post-independence government was elected in August 1980. Civil unrest erupted between 1998 and 2003, when a feud developed between the indigenous Isatabus who formed the Isatabu Freedom Movement (IFM) and the Malaitans, who had migrated from nearby Malaita since the end of the Second World War. Many Malaitans had jobs in the capital city, Honiara, located on Guadalcanal, the largest of the Solomon Islands group. This had caused resentment among the Isatabus. The IFM aimed to drive the Malaitans off Guadalcanal and the escalating hostilities resulted in a low-level civil war. During 1998, a militia group calling itself the Guadalcanal Revolutionary Army (GRA) set about evicting and harassing Malaitan settlers. In 1999, in response to the ethnic violence and expulsions, a rival Malaitan militia group was founded, the Malaita Eagle Force (MEF), led by Jimmy 'Rasta' Lusibaea, and the violence and bloodshed increased.

The Guadalcanal Liberation Front (GLF), an indigenous militia rebel group led by warlord Harold Keke and his right-hand man Ronnie Cawa, had grown steadily since independence. The GLF was based on the remote and resource-poor Weathercoast, located on the south coast of Guadalcanal. Claiming that he was fighting the Malaitans for the independence of his people, Keke and his followers led a four-year rampage of murder, hostage-taking, village raids and intimidation. Between them, these rebel militia groups drove more than twenty thousand Malaitans out of Guadalcanal. Several hundred people were murdered during the hostilities.

In June 2000, the MEF forced Prime Minister Bartholomew Ulufa'alu to resign and seized control of Honiara. The rival groups agreed to a ceasefire and signed the Townsville Peace Agreement in October 2000. Although most arms were not surrendered, a civil war was averted. Elections took place, but lawlessness reigned until July 2003 when Prime Minister Sir Allan Kemakeza, who was elected in December 2001, formally requested armed intervention from Australia. The five years of violence and extortion by the armed rival militia groups and their increasing demands for financial compensation from the government, the customary method of resolving disputes, had resulted in economic devastation, corruption in the government and police force and a breakdown in law and order.

On 24 July 2003, an Australian-led 2300-strong force landed in the Solomon Islands. This was the Regional Assistance Mission to Solomon Islands (RAMSI) on Operation *Helpem Fren* (pidgin English for 'help a friend'). The force was made up of 1400 Australian troops, as well as troops from New Zealand, Tonga, Fiji and Papua New Guinea. By Christmas that year, RAMSI, led by police and with military backing, had restored law and order and jailed militant leaders and corrupt officials. RAMSI also kept the finance and treasury departments under guard. Demands for payment ceased and gradually normality returned.

Between July and October 2003, the RAMSI intervention resulted in 3700 weapons being handed in under a gun amnesty and the arrest of several key rebel figures, including the most notorious warlord, former Special Constable and Armourer of the Royal Solomon Islands Police, Harold Keke, allegedly responsible for dozens of deaths, including that of seven members of the Melanesian Brotherhood, known to the locals as *Tasiu*. Also arrested were MEF leader Jimmy 'Rasta' Lusibaea and Moses Su'u.

Now investigative teams were needed to investigate and ultimately prosecute perpetrators of the war crimes committed on both sides of the factions. The first round of exhumations and autopsies took place in September 2003.

As I sit in my room in Honiara's Kitano Mendana hotel recording the first chapter of my activities in the Solomon Islands, the air-conditioner is roaring in the background and already the temperature and humidity are climbing. It is the second anniversary of the intervention of the Regional Assistance Mission to Solomon Islands (RAMSI), which occurred on 24 July 2003 and there have been celebrations at the RAMSI base for several days now.

This is my eighth trip to the Solomon Islands. For five of these trips I was involved in direct forensic investigation, and for three I have acted as an expert forensic witness in the trials of both militia killings and contemporary homicides. I know the staff at the hotel well by now, and on each occasion I am welcomed back like an old friend.

## SEPTEMBER 2003

In early September 2003, Associate Professor David Ranson received a phone call from the Australian Federal Police (AFP). They needed a forensic pathologist to go to the Solomon Islands to perform three autopsies with a turnaround of about a week. David had other commitments and was unable to help. Because of my extensive experience in East Timor and Kosova and my love of overseas forensic work, he approached me as the most likely candidate for this mission. I immediately and enthusiastically agreed to go and he gave me a contact number in Canberra. I didn't want a repeat of the East Timor experience where I had to work without the assistance of an experienced forensic technician, so I asked for an additional person to accompany me. To my relief, this was promptly granted.

Caroline de Koning is arguably one of the most experienced forensic technicians to come out of the Victorian Institute of Forensic Medicine (VIFM). Caro, as she prefers to be called, is friendly and lively, dedicated, driven and easy to work with. Caro came to the VIFM after spending a short time in the funeral industry. We have performed hundreds of autopsies together and I regard her as a great personal friend, above and beyond a work colleague.

I managed to track her down in the homicide room where she was reconstructing a body and asked whether she would like to go to the Solomon Islands as my forensic technician. She immediately agreed. We spent the five days remaining before our departure deciding on what to take with us. My experience in East Timor had taught me to bring with me all of the surgical instruments necessary to complete the autopsies. Being a traditional 'blood and guts' pathologist, I already had a collection of instruments. The small black case fitted neatly into a flight bag. I extracted the most useful headings from the United Nations (UN) autopsy pro-forma I had used in East Timor and created a unique RAMSI pro-forma for the examination of both decomposed and intact bodies. I packed many copies of this form and my dictaphone, tapes and batteries. By Monday 8 September we were ready to go.

Caro's family had driven her to the airport, and we met in the departure hall. In addition to her own personal luggage, she had a bag full of surgical scrubs, plastic aprons, rubber gloves and other supplies. During the check-in process, Caro met up with an old friend who worked for Qantas and we were upgraded to business class for the Melbourne to Brisbane leg of the journey. This was a pleasant surprise and a good start to what would prove to be a difficult but satisfying mission. We relished the larger, comfortable seats and generous breakfast and I was surprised to learn that Caro was an airline food addict. We arrived at Brisbane airport and, after passing through customs, indulged in some duty free purchases, mainly several litres of vodka to see us through the evenings we would spend in Honiara, the capital of the Solomon Islands.

We boarded the small Air Vanuatu aircraft for the three-hour flight to Honiara. As the craft flew over the island of Guadalcanal we could see below us, beneath a thick layer of cloud, a broad expanse of hundreds of acres of palm plantations and, behind them, tall mountains, deep escarpments and many conspicuous bright green bare hills. It reminded me very much of East Timor.

The plane landed at Henderson International Airport. As the exit door opened, we were hit by a blast of hot and humid air. We queued in the arrival hall, waiting for our passports to be checked, the intensity of the humidity in the building becoming almost unbearable. Within minutes, we were sweating profusely. Caro loves tropical conditions. As I became more and more uncomfortable, she became more and more animated. Fortunately for me, we didn't have to wait long.

When we entered the main hall of the airport. Detective Inspector John McIntyre, Inspector Craig Petterd and Paul Williams, all from RAMSI, were there to greet us. John McIntyre was the team leader of the investigations section of RAMSI. He is an imposing figure, with a strong and enthusiastic personality. Love him or hate him, all members of the AFP who know John bow to his experience and respect him highly for his organisational skills. We clicked immediately. During the following week, and indeed the following two missions (October 2003 and January 2004), I would work closely with John. We have become firm friends.

We packed our luggage onto the back of a RAMSI 4WD and headed off for a quick visit to Guadalcanal Beach Resort (GBR) at Red Beach in Honiara. Before being occupied by RAMSI, the site was a small, privately run beach resort with a large open building and several small beachside cabins. It was now the base occupied predominantly by the Australian army and a small number of AFP and New Zealand Police (NZPOL) personnel. We drove to the compound along what was to become known fondly as Ramsi Street, and showed our security passes to the two local security guards. We were to find out that we could get in just as easily, especially at night, by producing a packet of anti-malarial tablets, personal business cards, a box of teabags or even a Medicare card. This was treated as a bit of a joke and a challenge, but in the months to come security became tighter and we could only get in with a bona-fide security pass.

GBR reminded me of a scene from *MASH*. Next to the main building, acres of khaki-coloured canvas tents housed hundreds of soldiers. The main building was a mess hall with an area set aside for computer access and limited shopping. That was about it. The beach immediately behind the building had been cleared of live ordnance, but beyond its perimeter barbed wire had been erected to prevent access because of the danger of live ammunition. The beachfront was beautiful, with fine, grey sand. The waves slapped upon the beach and for as far as I could see a broad expanse of coconut palms gently led towards the ocean.

After introductions to other AFP members and a quick cup of coffee, John drove us to our hotel. Solomon Islands' Kitano Mendana hotel is one of the older and more established resorts on the island of Guadalcanal. It is located at Point Cruz, a jutting peninsula housing a wharf where two navy patrol boats were berthed. Our rooms, basic but comfortable, were immediately on the beachfront, which was lovely. The electricity was intermittent, so the air-conditioner stopped and started and we suffered more mosquito bites in the hotel room than we were to on the Weather-coast. Cockroaches came at no extra charge. Caro's room had a dank pool of water soaking into the carpet from someone leaving the small refrigerator door open.

There were no arrangements for the remainder of the day, so we went for a swim in the pool overlooking the beach. John picked us up that evening to take us to a barbecue at Iron Bottom Sound, so-called because of the large number of sunken American and Japanese navy vessels. It is now a haven for scuba divers. There was a get-together every Tuesday night, and it was a great opportunity for us to meet key RAMSI personnel, including Ben McDevitt, Commander of the Participating Police Forces. Ben, enthusiastic and dedicated, welcomed us warmly, thanking us for our assist-ance. After eating, and drinking several rounds of the local beer, John, Caro and I parted from the main crowd and chatted for a while on the jetty overlooking the ocean. By this time, the sun had gone down, and there was a gentle sea breeze, which was pleasant, but didn't reduce the humidity.

John wouldn't talk about the details of the mission, saying that a mandatory full briefing would be held on the afternoon of 11 September. As we chatted, we could tell that he was all fired up to undertake this mission and expected us to deliver the goods. He told us that we were to visit two sites on the Weathercoast. The first site was a double grave at Marasa beach. The second site was a single grave located at Sughu village. We would fly into the jungle by helicopter and set up a base camp. From there we would head into the jungle to exhume the bodies and perform the autopsies onsite. Among other essential exhumation equipment, we would have two wooden trestle-tables, we would use one as an instrument table and the other as the autopsy table. Other than that, he gave little away. Caro and I returned to the hotel where we sat up until the early hours of the morning chatting and drinking vodka.

John picked us up at seven o'clock the following morning and, after passing through security, we headed to the mess hall to join the large number of soldiers who were having their breakfast. In spite of the rather spartan conditions of the base, the army, as always, produced a sumptuous array of breakfast options. At the end of the food race, there was a large, plastic container filled with blister packs of Doxycycline. Doxycycline, or 'Doxy', as it is fondly called, is the anti-malarial medication issued to personnel in the Solomon Islands. The staff freely talked about the unexpected side effects of this medication. They called them 'Doxy moments'. I knew from my GP years that the common side effects included nausea, vomiting, diarrhoea, occasional skin rashes and, more rarely, photosensitivity. But I didn't know that lapses in concentration and short-term memory were also common. Apparently, people had moments of vagueness, stopping in the middle of a sentence and not remembering what they were about to say. This side effect isn't listed or known by general practitioners. It could be due in part to the tropical climate coupled with borderline dehydration, stress and a heavy workload. I would soon have my own experience of this side effect; I suffered many Doxy moments while I was in the Solomon Islands.

On one side of the mess hall, there was a rack for heavy calibre automatic weapons and ammunition belts. To our embarrassment,

Caro managed to trip on a large machine gun that was resting on the floor next to one of the soldiers. She quickly and humbly apologised for this mishap, and for a moment I was pleased that it was her and not me. The soldier accepted it as a simple accident, but glared in our general direction during our meal, making us feel a bit self-conscious.

Craig offered to drive us back to the hotel and suggested that we drop into the National Referral Hospital at Honiara to inspect the mortuary facility. The National Referral Hospital is a broad expanse of single-storey buildings arranged in a rather ramshackle way. It has the usual general and specialist wards, an operating theatre and a rudimentary pathology laboratory and x-ray facility. Many people were already waiting outside the hospital for consultations or medication. Craig ushered us behind the large, unsealed, dusty carpark at the front of the hospital towards a small concrete building no larger than a standard garage that could have been a storage area or woodshed.

He led us through a small annexe, just large enough for a car, and warned me that I would probably be disappointed with the mortuary. But we were delighted with what we saw as we stepped into the room. Although small, the mortuary contained a dedicated refrigerated unit, two laminated bench areas with shelving, two sinks with running water and a large old-fashioned white porcelain autopsy table. The overhead fluorescent lighting was adequate and, to my joy, there was an air-conditioning unit in the wall at the foot end of the autopsy table. What more could we possibly need? Although the mortuary itself was filthy, I told Craig that this would be more than adequate for our future post-mortem examinations. I was to spend many, many hours in this tiny facility in the years to come.

The air-conditioning was adequate, although it moved the air around rather than cooled it. But there was a large gaping space in the ceiling that needed to be repaired and the room was rather cramped. As well as pathologist and technician, the room would have to accommodate the scene-of-crime officer, photographer and two or more observers. There was no seating area for the observers other than a large blue trunk owned by the mortuary assistant which lay in front of the refrigerator. We would have to close the doors during the autopsies to prevent flies coming into the room. With up to six or seven hot, sweaty bodies in the room, things would get pretty close.

The following morning, we had another early morning trip to GBR to put our gear together for the following three days. Inside the entrance to the mess hall, there were two large, blue plastic containers laid out for our inspection. Caro and I had been assigned one each. The containers held all of the camping gear necessary for an extended stay in the jungle. Craig advised us to lighten the load by pooling our resources and putting all the necessities into one container. We emptied the containers and into one we placed our mosquito domes, groundsheets, inflatable pillows, a small camp oven, cutlery, cups and two torches. Unpacking and repacking into one container took some time. We then placed all the unwanted items into the second container to be stored for any further missions.

Caro and I were left to fill in the time until the mandatory briefing. We did a bit of exploring, and then, out of sheer boredom, we invented a game called 'hit the coconut'. This involved picking up ten pebbles each and placing a coconut shell about three metres away from where we were sitting. The aim of the game was to throw our stones in turn and keep score on who hit the coconut. It was childish, but we managed to while away the time. To Caro's chagrin, I managed to win every time.

Later that afternoon, in a tent set aside from the mess hall, John gave a presentation on the cases we were about to investigate.

He outlined and introduced all the personnel who would be involved in this taxing mission. He introduced us to the team and once again thanked us for our commitment. John's presentation was indeed impressive. It consisted of on-ground and aerial views of the dig site and also of the villages during the monsoon. One photograph showed a lake of water above which the roofs of huts could be seen. We hoped the rain would hold off, as this was certainly not a climate conducive to the exhumation of bodies. While the weather had held so far, we were told that we could expect torrential rainfall at any time. The Weathercoast is located on the south coast of Guadalcanal and is so-called because of its unique meteorological pattern. Depending on whom you believe, it can receive anything from five to ten metres of rainfall a year. The northern coast of the island only gets the seasonal monsoon rains.

Displaying his formidable organisational skills, John described the alleged offences and used maps to outline the stages of the mission in very fine detail. The reports relating to the background of the cases we were about to investigate were truly horrifying. On 15 June 2003, the Royal Solomon Islands Police (RSIP) sent two boats from Honiara to Marasa Bay in Guadalcanal to take provisions and cash to the Joint Operation Group (JOG) who were searching for Harold Keke, leader of the Guadalcanal Liberation Front (GLF). The JOG was made up of former members of the warring Isatabu Freedom Movement (IFM) and Malaita Eagle Force (MEF), as well as dedicated members of the community who wished to assist with policing. These individuals were trained to be special constables. The government intended to help the members of militant groups work together, as well as with other community members, to create a more cooperative society. But one of the consequences of the formation of the JOG was to further increase existing hostilities, resulting in violent clashes between the various factions.

On arriving at Marasa Bay, the group were ambushed and RSIP Special Constable David Vae was shot dead by members of the GLF while attempting to flee in a small, outboard-powered dinghy. According to witness statements, the following day, members of the GLF abducted approximately four hundred and twenty villagers of Marasa and walked them to the beach. Ex-Special Constable John Lovana and a local seventeen-year-old man were accused of being government spies and allegedly assaulted with rocks, sticks and rifle butts. About eleven thousand dollars had been taken from the captured vessel and had been torn up by the members of the GLF. Witnesses reported that the captors then forced the shredded money down the throats of the victims with sticks and forced them to dance and assault each other. Then they beat them for hours until they died.

The captive villagers were forced to watch the entire ordeal and were then made to dig graves to bury the two men. Witnesses reported that the GLF then kept the villagers hostage while they burnt ninety-two houses to the ground, finally releasing them on 18 June. The two victims of the alleged assault and torture were buried in a marked grave on Marasa beach and the victim of the alleged shooting, David Vae, had later been buried at Sughu village. We were sickened by the allegations, and hoped that our work would assist in the prosecution of the perpetrators of such horrific violence.

## BIG TOYS

Caro and I were told to return to Red Beach at five thirty in the afternoon to load our luggage onto the vessel to be transported to HMAS *Manoora*. HMAS *Manoora* and her sister ship HMAS *Kanimbla* were originally built for the United States Navy and were bought by the Royal Australian Navy in 1994. Their primary roles are to transport, lodge ashore and support an army contingent of four hundred and fifty troops, their vehicles and equipment. They are equipped with helicopter hangars capable of supporting up to four Army Blackhawks, or three of the larger Navy Sea King helicopters. The huge craft weighs 8534 tonnes and is 159.2 metres in length. They are big toys!

We would stay on the *Manoora* overnight and then a Sea King helicopter would drop us into the jungle at Marasa village, where we would set up a base camp, exhume the two bodies and perform the post-mortems onsite. A full autopsy at a jungle gravesite had never been done before. We would then go to Sughu village further along the Weathercoast to do the third and final autopsy.

The team assembled at five thirty on the beach, ready to embark. A large amount of equipment was piled up ready to be loaded. The team consisted of twenty-one personnel, made up of AFP, NZPOL, RSIP and VIFM staff who would act as scene-of-crime officers and investigators. Some would be taking witness statements from the local villagers who had been forced under duress to witness the atrocities we were about to investigate. A heavily armed contingent of eleven military personnel had also assembled. The lance corporal of this section was a young man who looked no older than sixteen but was a highly experienced and well-respected soldier. A minister of religion was also coming with us. He had apparently been held captive, wrapped in canvas and left overnight in a boat with his hands tied during the barbaric acts allegedly committed by Keke's men at Marasa. Fortunately for him, he had been released after the killings with the surviving villagers. His role on this trip was to provide spiritual guidance to the distressed villagers and to preside over a formal burial ceremony of the slain victims after the post-mortem examinations had been completed.

As the amphibious landing craft pulled out from the beach and turned about to face the *Manoora* anchored several kilometres offshore, a large wave hit the bulkhead, soaking many of us and the luggage. I took the full brunt of the wave—not a great start. Once it had docked with the stern of the *Manoora*, we crossed the small, rocking bridge into the cavernous belly of the ship. After all the equipment was loaded, we made our way up a labyrinth of small, steeply inclined metal staircases and were shown our accommodation for the night. Caro was lucky enough to be accommodated in the sleeping quarters of the medical unit with the other female personnel, while I was shown a rather spartan bunk where the ordinary navy crew slept. After a meal in the mess, Caro and I sat on the flight deck and took in the panoramic views of Guadalcanal. The island stretched before us under heavy clouds. There were many small fires on the shore, contributing to the heavy haze covering the island.

After breakfast the next morning, we gathered at the muster area next to the flight deck. The large Sea King helicopter waited for us on the flight deck. A further craft had been lashed down to the deck, its large blades folded back and tied to the tail rotor. We all put on large life preservers and listened to a short set of the usual instructions on how the life preservers worked. Then, casually, 'We are flying over water, and will be dropping you off on land. There are two unlikely possibilities. One is that we will crash into water. If this happens, grab the person to your right and then head left, wait until the cabin fills with water, open the cabin door, inflate your life vests and swim to safety. The second scenario is that we crash on land. Wait until the metal stops flying through the cabin and, if you are still alive, get the hell out of there.' Great.

MARASA

We waited our turn to board the helicopter, the largest one I have ever been in. We sat up the front behind the pilot where we could look out through one of the few portholes in the cabin. The trip took no more than ten minutes and we landed next to a small creek bed, about half a kilometre from Marasa. We unloaded our luggage from the craft and gathered on the edge of the creek. Within moments, the aircraft was again airborne and disappeared from view. I couldn't understand why the helicopter had chosen to land this side of the creek leaving us to haul our luggage across the swiftly flowing, knee-deep cold water to get to the other side. But I was told that the helicopters are so large that if they landed closer to the village the rotor wash would be strong enough to knock down the village huts. Having wet feet was better than destroying the community again.

We followed a well-worn track through the jungle to an open area where a large rectangular building that looked like a farm shed stood. The local villagers had graciously offered us the use of their church as our muster point. The church was a simple structure with a concrete half wall and a rusted tin roof. Immediately next to the church building, many small, thatched huts had been rebuilt since Keke's men had allegedly destroyed the village. Small, round stones surrounded neatly swept dirt areas around the huts.

The church was large enough to accommodate all but a small number of our group once we had put up the mosquito domes. Equipment boxes and other sundries were stored at the front of the building near the altar. The rest of our equipment, including the larger items, such as the wooden trestle-tables, metal picket posts and hessian bagging, were being brought over on HMAS *Tarakan*, which we would meet later at Marasa beach.

It was still early and we made our way directly to the gravesite to begin work. The bodies were buried approximately a hundred and fifty metres inland from the beach near to where the victims had reportedly been killed in full view of the villagers. The hike to the site took a little under an hour. We passed grassy open areas, thick, almost impenetrable jungle and a small well-worn track along a creek bed. While we waited for the *Tarakan* to arrive with our gear, one of the team noticed a small remnant of a Solomon Island five-dollar note lying beneath one of the boulders. Within minutes, we recovered many similar fragments. Although the atrocities had occurred in June, the tattered paper had been preserved on the beach all this time. These fragments strongly substantiated the witnesses' accounts of these horrendous events.

When the *Tarakan* arrived, we unloaded the rest of our equipment and broke into two groups. One group took further supplies back to the church and the other carried the gear to the exhumation site. The gravesite was within a short walking distance from a small creek. It was marked by three parallel cut branches in a clearing about the size of a living room. Surrounding this area was thick jungle, littered with boulders and fallen coconuts. There were also large nuts sprouting sharp vertical spears, which Caro called 'tripoponuts'. Although the dense jungle provided shade, the heat and humidity were oppressive.

As Caro set up the table for our equipment, pro-formas and cameras, John and I and several others photographed the site, drew a sketch map and, as this was a crime scene, cordoned off the perimeter of the gravesite with metal picket posts and hessian bags. Army personnel were not allowed to enter the crime scene, but were able to watch from outside.

We began digging and immediately had trouble. Marasa beach consists of small and medium-sized pebbles and boulders mixed with grey sand. The soil type inland at the gravesite was exactly the same. Our shovels were only able to remove the loose surface material and vegetation. We had to remove the small pebbles by hand and trowel to the depth of about a metre or so.

After about an hour of this gruelling work, we were relieved to detect the telltale odour of decomposing flesh and, shortly after, uncovered the first body part. I lowered myself into the pit with a hand trowel and carefully began to expose the body. The edge of the pit occasionally fell in, hampering our progress. After a long time, we finally had the first body fully exposed.

The lightly-clad man was lying on his back; his companion, still partially covered, lay next to him. We photographed the two bodies and then removed the first body from the pit and placed it in a body bag. Meanwhile, Caro had set up the instrument table with impressive precision, methodically laying out all of the instruments in the order I would need them and, on the other side of the table, small specimen containers for any evidential material I might recover. The second wooden table for the autopsy stood next to it. I could have been about to perform an autopsy on an operating table in a sophisticated theatre suite instead of on a trestle-table in the middle of the jungle.

By around three o'clock, we were ready to begin the first autopsy. We placed the body on the wooden table and photographed it from all angles. I then began the external examination. I had decided it would be more efficient to dictate my findings into the dictaphone as I would at home. I'd be able to transcribe my findings into an interim written post-mortem report later on.

The dark-skinned body had turned white from partial decomposition. The clothing matched the witnesses' description exactly. Both men were of similar stature, so this evidence was of great benefit in the initial stages of identification. I then moved on to the internal examination. The body was well enough preserved to approach the autopsy in a conventional way. Although much of the internal organs had largely broken down, the trauma to the skeleton was obvious. Because this matter is sub judice, I can't describe in detail what I found, but can say that the injuries were extreme, lethal and correlated precisely with the witness statements from the villagers.

I finished the first autopsy after about an hour and we organised a bucket brigade to collect water from the nearby creek to wash the table down. We were losing light quickly, so we decided to begin the second autopsy the next morning. We covered the second body with a tarpaulin and partially reburied it to prevent any marauding animals from feeding on the corpse during the night. Many village pigs roamed the area and bush rats were everywhere, so a soldier was posted to guard the perimeter during the night. When everything was in order, we packed up our instruments and headed back to the village. We were told the next day that several pigs had entered the gravesite and that only stones had been thrown.

An area had been set aside at the back of the church for cooking our army ration packs. The 'rat-packs', as they are known contain precooked meals that can be eaten either hot or cold, tins of cheese and condensed milk, dry and sweet biscuits, tubes of Vegemite and jam and other things like matches, chewing gum and an unusual implement known fondly by the army personnel as 'Fred', which stood for 'fucking ridiculous eating device'. It had a can opener at one end and a spoon at the other. Fred was difficult to master and I was in danger of slicing my thumb off trying to open the small tin cans. I was never able to use Fred successfully and had to ask one of the army guys to open my tins for me. Annoyingly, multi-skilled Caro found Fred easy to manipulate. That night, we ate lukewarm spaghetti and meatballs, followed by cheese and biscuits and a cup of coffee. We spent the rest of the evening chatting to the army guys and taking in the serene environment.

There were no toilet facilities other than the broad expanse of jungle surrounding us. I didn't want to inadvertently wander into somebody's backyard, so, with toilet roll in hand, I asked one of the villagers where the local toilet area might be. My query seemed to cause great amusement and the man escorted me up a small track about three quarters of a kilometre from the base camp. He ushered me down a further sidetrack and showed me an area within the dense jungle. I made my way in, stepping carefully around the small mounds of both fresh and degrading human excrement distributed at random, to avoid stepping in any of these deposits. My privacy was not invaded by anyone, luckily. My guide insisted on waiting for me so that I wouldn't get lost on the way back and we made our way back together. Caro had a similar experience, but was shown a separate area for the women. We both laughed about it later.

Later that evening, several of the team decided to have a quick dip and wash in one of the nearby shallow creeks. As we were cooling off in the stream, we noticed a group of villagers about twenty metres downstream from us. The women were washing vegetables in the stream for the evening meal. Out of nowhere, a pig appeared in the sky and landed in the stream. We couldn't hear any squeals from the pig and we realised that it had been barbecued and tossed into the creek to cool down. We then pondered the situation. We were downstream from the toilet and upstream from the locals preparing their meal. Which scenario could be worse?

The army guys were a happy bunch and were pleased to break their boredom at GBR by protecting the investigative team. One of them demonstrated his Ninox night vision gear. It fits firmly to the face and beneath the chin and totally transforms the night terrain. Against a background of dark green, all foreground structures are bright green. Moths and small animals scuttling through the jungle are clearly visible. Instead of the few stars normally visible to the naked eye, I could see a myriad of glowing small pinpoints of light.

The moon was too bright to look at directly. His Steyr rifle had infrared targeting. When he pointed his rifle into the jungle, the target was indicated by a white spot in the night vision gear. All he had to do was squeeze the trigger and he would hit the target. It was all very impressive. After a bit of small talk and a last cup of coffee, we retired for the night.

The atmosphere inside the small church building was like a sauna. There was little in the way of a breeze and the humidity was stifling. Although the open weave of the mosquito dome was designed to allow a breeze to pass through, it actually seemed to contain the humidity and accentuate it. Lucky Caro was near the rear entrance of the building and had the benefit of any light breeze that passed through.

During the small hours of the morning, a blood-curdling scream came from the village. The screaming was unrelenting, and seemed to come from a woman in distress. Although many of the team slept through this, Caro and I and many others sat bolt upright and wondered what could be going on. The heavily armed soldier who patrolled the building at all times went off to investigate. It turned out that one of the local villagers' children was profoundly retarded and was prone to screaming outbursts during the night. This was a very unsettling experience.

The following morning, we returned to the gravesite, and extracted the second body from the ground. Again, catastrophic injuries were evident and the findings correlated well with the witness statements. This victim had several elaborate tattoos, which were clearly apparent against the whitened skin. A tattooed centipede wrapped itself around his forearm and elbow and there was also a crucifix and a heart. They would not have been obvious against dark skin, but the effects of decomposition made them obvious and meant we could easily distinguish one body from the other. We finished just before eleven o'clock and, after cleaning up and putting away the instruments, we had a quick lunch break at a small, open shed about fifty metres from the gravesite.

It was time for the two men to finally have a dignified and Christian burial. Their bodies were placed into two coffins that had been brought along for this purpose. Many of the villagers and members of the immediate family gathered at the small cemetery near the shed and the Reverend, who had come with us, presided over the ceremony, both in English and in pidgin. After the formal part of the service, the Reverend thanked us for our efforts and acknowledged the terrible work we had undertaken. The coffins were lowered into the graves and the last rites given. The family members threw soil and pebbles into the graves, the sound of the small rocks hitting the coffin lid resounding like gunfire. The villagers began to grieve and wail in their traditional fashion. They had been prevented by their captors from doing this at the time their loved ones were murdered, under the threat of death. It was their moment to unleash all of the pent-up grief and pain that they had harboured since June. It was an incredibly emotional time for those of us looking on; we were openly moved by the service. Caro and I stood by the gravesite in silence, but then I moved away from the gathering and sat quietly by the shed. Many others did the same. There was no small talk, the mood was extremely sombre, and we all felt the pain of the local villagers.

## MAN PLANS, GOD LAUGHS

We packed up the luggage and equipment and set off on our return journey to the church at Marasa. The pathway from the beach to the village had many obstacles—heavy, fallen vines (which Caro called 'stupid roots'), a myriad of coconuts, slippery rocks and thick vegetation—so the army had bulldozed a track, a road that had not existed for forty years. We took the new route, laden with backpacks and, in my case, camera equipment and medical instruments.

What happened next seemed to happen in slow motion. I caught the toe of my boot on a 'stupid root' just below the surface of the newly loosened soil. I lurched forward in a somersault and took the impact of the fall on my left wrist. My packs flew into the air and scattered right and left. I felt a klunk in my elbow and a searing pain down my forearm into my wrist. I knew I had broken a bone. I was acutely embarrassed.

John asked me if I was okay and I said it was only a sprain and that I would be fine. He didn't conceal his disbelief; he could tell by my face that I was not being entirely truthful. He suggested I go back by helicopter to the *Manoora* for first-aid, but I couldn't bring myself to do this. I felt that a simple undisplaced fracture was not enough to justify leaving. If I did I would be letting myself, my team, the victims and the villagers down. I assured him that it was only a sprain and that everything was fine. But the pain was increasing and within the hour my elbow had swollen to twice its size and had developed a nasty bluish-black hue. I wasn't able to move my elbow, wrist or fingers and my fingertips were tingling. I knew I had suffered a fracture, probably at the head of the radius, which is one of the two bones of the forearm.

John picked up all the strewn equipment and added it to his own gear. The extra load didn't worry him. I made my way as best I could back to the village with the others and searched for the small first-aid kit. There was no analgesia to help with the pain, but I found a length of bandage and formed a figure-of-eight sling. The pain meant that I couldn't open any of the food packets on my own, or prepare my groundsheet and pillow in the mosquito dome. As Caro helped me out, I confided to her that I had almost certainly fractured my arm and wasn't sure how we would get on with the final examination the following morning. She assured me that she would help in whatever way necessary. John quizzed me many times that evening about the degree of pain. We chose a scale of ten. I placed the level of discomfort at eight to nine, but quoted him three to four.

I tend to sleep on my left side, but that was impossible, and sleeping on my right side seemed to make the pain of the fracture worse. So I lay semi-reclined and awake for most of the night as the pain increased. I worried about the injury jeopardising the final stage of the mission and at about four o'clock, as an experiment, I tried to remove the cap of a previously opened water bottle. This small task was next to impossible. I had lost all power of grip and sensation.

The first question John asked me the next morning was how the pain was on the scale of one to ten. I said it was about two to three, nothing to worry about. He was sceptical, but it was my call and I was insistent, though not sure I had convinced him. I was to learn during our next mission that he had fully suspected the extent of the injury and called me a bastard for pushing on.

SUGHU

After a short breakfast, we returned to the gravesite and gathered on the beachfront, where the *Tarakan* waited to transport us to Sughu. At Sughu we would undertake the final exhumation and autopsy of the third body, RSIP Special Constable David Vae. The *Tarakan*, a large amphibious landing craft, was waiting for us. It was designed to transport heavy vehicles and troops in times of war and had seen action in East Timor. The equipment was placed on deck in an unceremonious pile and we got on board. For the next hour or so, we enjoyed the views of the beach and jungle vista unfolding before us. The sea was calm and there was a light breeze to relieve the heat and humidity. The sun was scorching, so a tarpaulin was erected across the deck for some shade.

As the *Tarakan* approached Sughu beach, John took me to one side and told me in a matter-of-fact way that the locals at Marasa had known we were coming and were happy for us to do our work. The villagers at Sughu, however, were not aware of our arrival and could be unhappy about it. He warned me that anything could happen. I managed to keep my composure, as though confronting hostile and possibly armed locals on their territory was something I was used to. The troops were ordered to lock and load and the eleven army personnel took up their arms. The *Tarakan* hit the beach, and the large drop gate at the bow descended with a crash. I went straight over to Caro and passed on what John had just told me. I warned her to keep her head down and pushed her down behind the bulkhead. Fortunately, our reception wasn't hostile and were able to disembark without incident.

After the troops disembarked, we followed and proceeded to unload the equipment onto the beach. I was not much help because of my arm. Despite the grim duty that lay ahead of us, we thought Sughu beach was a magical place. The beachfront was a mixture of sand and small pebbles and coconut palms gave way to dense jungle behind. Fortunately, the gravesite was little more than fifty metres inland and we found it in minutes. A clearing in the jungle marked the area of the gravesite and the disturbed soil was already producing a new, low-lying growth of foliage, which contrasted sharply with the otherwise undisturbed vegetation. The earth was firm, dark sand rather than the difficult pebbles and sand we had had to dig through in Marasa.

Caro assembled the two tables again close to the gravesite and laid out the essential equipment in preparation for the autopsy.

Again, we took photographs and drew up sketch plans. At that instant, there was a tremendous crash in the foliage near the tables. A coconut had just fallen from an overhanging palm. The coconuts were about fifteen metres above the ground and would seriously injure or even kill anyone they landed on. We moved the tables away from under the coconut palms.

This victim had allegedly been shot at Marasa and was later buried at Sughu. The witness statements said that a high-powered rifle had been discharged from a distance of approximately one hundred and fifty metres, hitting him in either the head or the neck. The outboard motor and stern of the boat that he had been in at the time he was shot had been peppered with bullet holes. From a cold, forensic point of view, I expected an easy result, which was a relief given that I could only use one arm. John told me that the body had been wrapped in a tent before it was buried and asked me what state of decomposition I expected. On the basis of the bodies we had exhumed at Marasa, I thought it would be in a relatively good state of preservation, particularly because it had been wrapped up after death before burial.

I couldn't have been more wrong! The grave was deep, and the others had dug to just over a metre and a half down before we noticed the smell of decomposition. The body was wrapped in a tent and bound by rope. As we unfolded the layers of the tent, we discovered that the remains of the victim were extensively decomposed. Instead of a well-preserved body, this was the other end of the spectrum of decomposition. The body may have been left above ground for a day or so before being wrapped up. Unlike the previous two, this body was in a semi-liquid state and many of the body parts were freely coming away from the torso. The smell of decomposition was overwhelming. At that moment, the head separated and began to roll back into the grave. With my one good arm, I lurched forward and caught it before it tumbled back in. Caro called it the catch of the day.

A certain amount of levity and black humour is absolutely essential in such tragic circumstances. It is not a sign of disrespect toward the dead, but rather a way of coping with circumstances that most people are never exposed to. John and I knelt together to examine the remains and I could see that he was affected by the odour in spite of his face-mask. I leaned over to him and whispered into his ear, 'Soft cock!' He leaned back towards me and, referring to my broken arm, asked me whether I had a problem with gravity. Touché! We knew that we could jerk each other's chain and get away with it. It was time to 'harden up', an expression we used often in these distressing circumstances.

Just then, the moment we had dreaded came upon us as the monsoon rains hit. It was white water. The soldiers erected a tent in less than ten minutes, which has to be some kind of record. The tent was small, just large enough to house the two instrument tables, Caro, several observers and myself. The rain was unrelenting, and within seconds, the roof of the tent bowed inwards with the weight of the fresh rainwater that freely spilled over the edges. There was no need now to organise a bucket brigade from the gravesite to the beach, as we had more water than we could possibly use. As we looked out of the tent into the jungle, we were amazed to see several soldiers standing under black umbrellas looking at us. They took a photograph of us, and we reciprocated.

Doing the best I could with my one good arm, I began the examination. If this man had been hit in the head with a high-velocity projectile, I should see obvious signs of trauma. I examined the cranium and jaw and quickly realised, for the bones were pristine, that there was no evidence of gunshot. In all probability, the bullet had hit the man in the neck and so I should see catastrophic injury to the spine. It was easy to separate the neck bones because of the advanced state of decomposition. This was fortunate given my broken arm. But we could not identify any injuries. It was possible that the bullet had passed through the soft tissues of the neck and that we would not find any evidence of injury. This finding would not necessarily contradict the evidence from the witness statements.

It was still necessary to perform a full examination of the total body. As I felt my way through the degraded remains of the man's upper right chest, my fingers hit something solid. I called to John to come over and look at the core of the bullet that I held in the palm of my hand.

'Hey, Johnno, come over here! I just found the bullet!'

'Oh, fuck off, mate, no way!'

'No, mate, it's right here. Come and have a look.'

'Mate, mate! That is the icing on the cake!'

Several minutes later, I found the fragments of the copper jacketing of the bullet in the same region.

'Hey, Johnno, come and have a look at this!'

'What, mate?'

'I've just found the bullet jacket.'

'Oh, fuck off!'

'No, mate, we've now got bullet and jacket. Mission accomplished!'

'Mate! That is now the cherry on the icing on the cake!'

We were both over the moon that I had found hard, ballistic evidence. After reconstructing the entry point, it was clear that the man had been in a crouched and rotated position when he was hit by the bullet. He was probably trying desperately to start the outboard engine. I couldn't be sure why the bullet had not passed through his body. It could have been because old or faulty ammunition reduced the velocity of the discharge, but, whatever the reason for that, we had now established a firm cause of death. I was pleased that we had managed to extract definitive evidence that could be analysed and presented in court.

We completed the autopsy in just under an hour and a half. Caro was indispensable. I had realised on reaching Sughu that the blue boiler suit I had brought with me was far too heavy and clingy and I opted for a conventional pair of operating theatre scrubs to perform this last autopsy. As my left arm hung uselessly by my side, Caro had to help me out of the boiler suit and into the scrubs. She helped me put my hands into the rubber post-mortem gloves. Even putting on my right glove was difficult. But the most painful part of the process was removing the gloves at the end of the autopsy. With one quick jerk, she managed to peel off my left glove. The pain I felt at that instant was excruciating and for a moment I felt distinctly pale and sweaty.

I was very relieved that we had successfully completed this third case. The mission was complete; we had successfully examined all three victims, confirmed their identification and, in the last case, had retrieved vitally important ballistic evidence. All in all, it was a good morning's work. We cleaned up and packed the equipment back into the boxes to be returned to storage.

The only remaining thing to do now was to give this man a Christian burial. Several of the RAMSI officers set about making a cross out of wood and rope. The body was placed in a coffin brought for the purpose. No villagers or family members attended this solemn service. The slain man was laid to rest and again the Reverend presided over the ceremony and administered the last rites. Although a very sad affair, we were at least spared the heart rending wailing that we had experienced the day before.

As the mission was drawing to a close, it was time now to

dispose of the items that we didn't want to bring back to base. We built a large bonfire on the beach next to where the *Tarakan* waited, and lit it. Then someone suggested a swim, so we made our way back onto the *Tarakan* and sailed out into the bay. The drop gate of the *Tarakan* was lowered, forming a diving platform into the cool, clear, blue water below. I was unable to join in because of my injured elbow, so I watched with envy as the others splashed about in the refreshing clear, dark blue water. A group swam twenty metres or so from the platform while the others watched. After about twenty minutes, Caro swam back to the platform and exclaimed that she had been bitten in places where a girl just shouldn't be bitten. Others also complained of small nibbles on their limbs, which had started to itch badly. We suspected sea lice.

Several of us chose to stay on board the *Tarakan* overnight, while the rest decided to camp on the beach and sleep in the open or in their mosquito domes. I stayed aboard and from the deck at night we could see the bonfire and hear the occasional burst of laughter as the soldiers and investigative team joked among themselves. One of our team had mentioned to the captain that I had probably broken my arm the previous day. The captain very graciously offered me the use of his cabin to have a shower. I gladly accepted. The small bathroom annexe was lined with stainless steel and it was with great effort that I managed to remove my sweat-laden t-shirt and shorts. My t-shirt was stuck to my back and it took several moments of painful contortions to get it off. After a quick shower, I got dressed again in the same clothes, again a very difficult task. I imagined that the captain would be wondering what the hell was going on, especially after I had been specifically instructed not to spend any more than four minutes under the shower.

The crew of the *Tarakan* were great. All the deck hands were very friendly and vitally interested in the mission we had just undertaken. I was fascinated by the two fifty-calibre Browning machine guns mounted on piers on either side of the wheelhouse. One of the crew instructed me in the use of the heavy calibre weapon and regretted that it was not possible to discharge it, as we were too close to shore. He showed Caro and me a homemade videotape of the gun in action, which was impressive, though I'm not sure Caro was quite as enthralled as I was.

We shared a hot meal with some of the crew and spent the rest of the evening on deck, taking in the balmy surroundings. The powerful searchlights on the deck of the *Tarakan* illuminated the water below. Caro and I were spellbound as we watched large sea snakes swimming past, attracted by the light, and masses of phosphorescent plankton. It was finally time for bed and we were shown to a small container that lay on deck immediately in front of the wheelhouse. This cramped container held six bunk beds. I crawled into the lower bunk, a space that was no more than half a metre in height. One of the crew offered me a tube of Dencorub to apply to my left arm, which I did. But unluckily this added to the pain; it was like throwing petrol on a fire. By now the movement in my fingers and wrist was returning, although it was still impossible to flex or extend my elbow. My elbow had puffed up considerably and much of my left forearm was blue-black in colour. I would have to seek medical attention and an x-ray examination as soon as we got back to Brisbane.

## BACK TO HONIARA

Early the next morning, we were awakened by the routine call through the PA system. 'Pip pip peeep! Wakey, wakey, wakey!' It was now time for the *Tarakan* to make the eight-hour return trip to Honiara and I thought this would be a good time to get the reports written up. I was offered the use of a small cabin with a desk and, after breakfast, I set about transcribing the post-mortem findings from the dictaphone into a written interim report while the rest of the team finalised their reports or lounged about on the deck. The boat pitched gently in the waves and occasionally the pen would roll off the table.

Then the Doxy moment hit. The dictaphone I had brought was the one I routinely use for post-mortem work back home. I use it in the mornings at the conclusion of each autopsy and in the afternoons for formal reports. I knew this instrument back to front, but here I was staring at it not able to remember which button to push. I didn't want to push the wrong button and erase any of my description. This lasted for several minutes. I would also put a form to one side and promptly lose it, even though it was in front of me the whole time. I found this very unsettling. After I had completed the first report, John came into the cabin to see how things were going. I told him about the dictaphone incident and misplacing the reports. He told me not to worry, that they were classic Doxy moments. Feeling a little reassured, I completed the final two reports over the next couple of hours and returned to the deck to join the others.

Unfortunately, while writing the reports, I had missed seeing some whales and schools of flying fish. Caro, a zoologist by training, was in her element. Because of the oppressive heat and humidity, she had elected to wear a pair of surgical scrubs. Just at that instant, a massive wave came over the deck and soaked her completely. We all agreed that she would have been an excellent candidate for a wet t-shirt competition. Another wave hit the deck with similar results. Caro couldn't stop laughing. As on previous missions, the wonderful interaction with the team members meant I didn't need a debrief at the end of the mission. No psychologists needed here!

Before long, the imposing silhouette of the *Manoora* loomed and land was in sight. A light amphibious landing craft docked with the *Tarakan* and, one by one, we embarked on the small vessel with our luggage and equipment. It was a bit tricky negotiating the two bobbing decks with only one arm in use for stability. The small craft finally dropped us back at Red Beach and we unloaded all the equipment. Our work was done.

HOME AGAIN

At four o'clock on Tuesday 16 September, we boarded the small Air Vanuatu jet bound for Brisbane. We spent a day in Brisbane for a bit of rest and relaxation and I had my arm x-rayed, which confirmed that the head of the radius had fractured and was slightly angulated. We spent the rest of the day walking around Brisbane and lounging poolside at the hotel.

Over the following weeks, I continued to function as usual at the Institute. I would perform several autopsies in the morning and do my routine microscope and office work in the afternoon. The fracture didn't impede my work greatly, although getting rubber gloves on and off was still an ordeal. At least it gave me a reason not to wear a necktie. But as my elbow was steadily improving, I noticed that the pain in my wrist was increasing. A further x-ray showed that the fracture of the head of the radius was in satisfactory condition, but an x-ray of my wrist disclosed a fracture of one of the small carpal bones. This would eventually heal with time, although the pain lingered well after the discomfort of the elbow had resolved itself.

Professor Stephen Cordner suggested that I must have created some kind of record. He thought that it was likely that I was the first forensic pathologist to perform an autopsy on a wooden plank in the middle of the jungle with a fractured forearm and he sug-

A view of the city of Honiara taken from the steps of Government House, October 2003.

The landing site of the Sea King helicopter near Marasa on the Weathercoast of Guadalcanal, September 2003.

Our jungle autopsy suite at the gravesite near Marasa beach, September 2003.

Caroline de Koning and I examining the first of the exhumed bodies at Marasa, September 2003.

The landing craft HMAS *Tarakan* at Marasa beach prior to our departure to Sughu on the Weathercoast, September 2003.

Caroline and I have just finished the post-mortem examination of an exhumed body at Sughu, September 2003. Moments before, we experienced a torrential monsoonal downpour.

Caroline in the mortuary at Honiara National Referral Hospital, October 2003. Caroline was not only an exceptional forensic technician but also an excellent travelling companion.

Several members of the forensic team after the completion of the second round of autopsies in the Solomon Islands, October 2003. L–R: Caroline de Koning, Adam Liversidge, Malcolm Dodd, Darren Folau, Tracey Young and Lisa Nicholson.

The mass grave at Ravu on the Weathercoast, May 2004.

Dr Melanie Archer, Consultant Forensic Entomologist for the Victorian Institute of Forensic Medicine. Mel also proved to be an exceptional forensic technician. She is seen here at the Kitano Mendana Hotel in Honiara, pinning out specimens of rhinoceros beetles gathered from Henderson airfield. January 2004.

The Caribou on the airstrip at Mbambanakira, May 2004. This aircraft was invaluable in transferring exhumed bodies and equipment from the Weathercoast.

A view of Pite beach, the site of many exhumations on the Weathercoast, May 2004.

En route to the exhumation site near Chelu Village, January 2004.

Detective Inspector John McIntyre (aka PC Snappy Glove) of the
Australian Federal Police prepares to assist in the mortuary at the
Honiara National Referral Hospital, January 2004.
(Photo: Dr Mel Archer)

gested that I write this up as a case report, which are anecdotes that are sometimes included in our professional journals. I respectfully declined. Continuing the mission in such circumstances did win me brownie points with the RAMSI personnel back in the Solomon Islands, however.

In August 2005, I received an unexpected phone call from John McIntyre. He had called to inform me that the AFP, NZPOL, RSIP and the VIFM were the recipients of the Founder's Award of the International Homicide Investigators' Association on the basis of the mission and work performed at Marasa and Sughu. John (representing the AFP) and I (representing the VIFM) were named specifically in the presentation speech and citation. To emphasise the importance of this prestigious award, the previous year's recipients were the investigating team who tracked down the notorious and elusive Green River serial killer in the United States. The investigation in the Solomon Islands to date has resulted in eighteen militants from the GLF being removed from the Weathercoast. Several of them have faced trial and are now serving life sentences for related matters.

OCTOBER 2003

The second mission to the Solomon Islands was in October 2003. It was a highly publicised and emotionally charged case involving the slaying of seven members of the highly respected Anglican Melanesian Brotherhood in April 2003, allegedly by Keke's men. These particularly brutal murders had shocked the nation, as the Brothers had gained a reputation for their fearless peace efforts throughout the conflict. They actively promoted peace in the region, and camped between enemy lines, visiting and praying with both sides involved in the conflict and often putting themselves in the line of fire. They fearlessly encouraged the end to hostilities and had rescued kidnapped hostages. They had also become involved in the collection of weapons and they are believed to have saved many lives, as many people surrendered themselves and their weapons to them. While many believed the Brothers to be untouchable, as the hostilities escalated their position became increasingly perilous. Although the GLF had previously directed their hostilities to the Malaitans, they had begun to target their own people.

Three of the Brothers had taken a letter from the Anglican Archbishop to Harold Keke, as one of the Brothers, Nathaniel Sado, was known to him and wanted to make a personal appeal to stop the fighting. Brother Sado urged the others to return while he stayed to speak to Keke. Unable to convince him to return with them, the two Brothers did as he asked. Keke's men allegedly captured Brother Sado and accused him of being a government spy. He was tied up and imprisoned in the village of Pite. He later tried to escape, was captured and then reportedly beaten to death.

The following month, when Brother Sado didn't return, a further six Brothers decided to go to investigate what had happened and to recover his body. They never returned. Months later, the story of what had happened to the Brothers emerged. It was reported that as they approached Keke's camp they were confronted by Ronnie Cawa and his men, who allegedly shot three of them. The remaining three were marched at gunpoint back to the camp at Pite and allegedly killed after being interrogated and tortured by Ronnie Cawa, Owen Isa, Joses Kejoa and a youth whose name has been suppressed and is known only as 'K'.

I received a phone call from Detective Inspector Darren Folau of the NZPOL on 1 October 2003. Darren had accompanied us on our first mission to the Solomon Islands and had been appointed second in command in case anything happened to John McIntyre.

Darren was the team leader in the investigation and exhumation of the seven slain Melanesian Brothers and was calling to ask if I would be available to help. I immediately agreed. This was to be the beginning, for me, of a further four missions to the Solomon Islands to perform post-mortem examinations.

As Caro had proved to be an incredibly efficient forensic technician, and excellent travelling companion, I asked her whether she would like to go on this mission. She accepted immediately. As we had not long since left the Solomon Islands, there was little to do in the way of preparation for this next mission. I brought my personal post-mortem kit out of storage and restocked the anthropology pack. We flew out on Thursday 9 October, planning to return to Melbourne on 18 October.

We had a couple of hours to kill at the Brisbane international airport and while selecting duty free merchandise to see us on our way confused the actual departure time with the boarding time of the aircraft. Before long, we heard our names being paged again and again on the public address system. With bags in hand, we ran down the corridor towards the departure gate, incurring the wrath of the flight attendant as we hurriedly showed her our boarding passes and passports. As the aircraft took off, it took a while for our pulses to settle back to normal, as we thought about the ramifications of missing the flight. It would have been a very embarrassing situation and difficult to explain away.

Before long, we touched down at Henderson Airport. After going through customs and immigration and collecting our luggage, we were met at the arrival hall by Darren and several members of the AFP. Happily, John McIntyre was there again to greet us. His first question was 'How is the arm?' I told him that I had indeed fractured my elbow, but that now things were more or less back to normal. There was only some slight discomfort when I lifted anything. Another round of abuse from him was followed by a broad Johnno grin. Good job! They drove us to the Mendana Hotel and we checked in. We had the rest of the afternoon free, so in our usual style, we lounged by the pool and had a late meal. We would begin work the next morning, performing an autopsy on a fresh case that Darren had alerted me to before beginning the autopsies on the Brothers.

At nine o'clock the following morning, members of RAMSI picked us up and drove us directly to the mortuary at Honiara Referral Hospital. We were pleased to see that the large gaping area in the ceiling of the mortuary had been repaired with plywood. We hoped that this would reduce the numbers of flies and spiders. Several of the fluorescent lights had been replaced, greatly improving the lighting of the small, cramped facility.

## THE AIRPORT HOTEL 'MURDER'

We got straight to work and brought the body bag out from the refrigerator and laid it on the post-mortem table. The officers told me that this victim had died in the Airport Hotel and that a man had been arrested for his murder. The man had possibly been surprised while breaking into the hotel in an intoxicated state. He had then allegedly been stabbed in the neck by an assailant who had then fled the scene, but who had later given himself up to the police. The officer who attended the crime scene also indicated that the man had apparently crashed headfirst through a louvred window. There was an enormous amount of blood-spatter in the immediate area, along with many shards of broken glass. The circumstances surrounding the man's death were unclear, and it was possible that he had simply stumbled into the window while drunk. This could cause a forensic dilemma. I wasn't sure that we could readily distinguish between a wound caused by the action of a stabbing blade and that caused by a broken shard of glass.

I began the external examination of the body of this well-built man, which reeked of alcohol. I could see no evidence of any offensive or defensive type injuries. Specifically, there were no cuts or abrasions to the fingers, hands, or forearms. Nor were there any areas of trauma to the face. As a consequence of inhaling blood, there was a moderate amount of blood-stained frothy material around the nose and mouth. This man had not died immediately; the informants had indicated that he had walked around the room leaving heavy blood trails and bloody footprints before collapsing in an armchair.

After the initial photographs were taken, I closely inspected a single, large gaping wound to the right side of the man's neck. The injury had certainly been caused by a sharp item, perhaps a knife, but I thought it more likely to have been caused by a shard of glass. The sharp object had penetrated the carotid artery and passed completely through his larynx. At this critical point in the examination, the lights failed. We waited several seconds for the generator to kick back in, but it didn't. I rummaged around in my post-mortem bag and got out my halogen headlight. I turned it on and the lights flickered back on. I kept it on my head just in case.

Once we had light again, I examined the edges of the wound. My initial feeling was confirmed by the shelving present on the front edge of the wound. Shelving indicates that the blade or cutting object had undercut the skin at a very shallow angle, forming a thin, translucent layer of skin immediately above the deep cut. The edges of the wound were slightly ragged and irregular in places. These features are not normally seen after the plunging of a sharp blade, but are more in keeping with the rectangular, leading edge of broken glass.

I told the informants what I thought. My gut feeling, along with the nature of the wound, indicated that this man had probably died as a result of falling into the glass window, rather than as the result of deliberate stabbing by an assailant. The investigating team then told me that this was their feeling also. The man who had confessed to the alleged crime may well have been doing so under duress. In the months to come, I would return to the Solomon Islands to deliver my expert forensic opinion about the interpretation of the wound in this case. Several weeks before the trial began, the would-be assailant retracted his confession and claimed that he had been coerced into admitting to stabbing the man. The presiding judge found him not guilty of the crime on the basis of insufficient evidence to incriminate him and he was duly released.

After finishing this autopsy, we decided to return back to the hotel for some lunch, and begin the first of the seven missionary autopsies the next morning. After a light lunch, Caro and I walked around downtown Honiara. The city of Honiara is difficult to describe. It can be approached on a sealed road from the airport within about twenty minutes. The city itself is quite small and, at the time of our stay, quite dusty and dirty. The main town centre is a street with a single row of low-level buildings containing banks, shops and the occasional small, fresh coconut outlet, the equivalent to our milkbars at home. Immediately in front is the harbour, and behind, a series of heavily potholed, unsealed roads leading to several hotels and resorts. One area, called Chinatown, consists of a collection of shops all selling the same items. The dusty road and shanty town feel of the place resembles a scene from a Wild West movie. Travelling further west, the road changes from grossly degraded to well bituminised, leading to a series of small villages, and then it ends. The scenery surrounding Honiara, however, is magnificent.

After the intervention of RAMSI, normality had gradually

returned to the capital. Businesses were reopening and people had the confidence to go about their daily duties. The times of intimidation were waning. We felt reasonably safe walking around the town, but occasionally we would be greeted by odd glances from some of the local lads. On one occasion, we passed by a group of local youths and then heard the cry, 'Hey, white-arse!' It could have been wide-arse, we weren't sure. What we were sure of was the next exclamation, 'Hey bastard, fuck off!' We decided that discretion was the better part of valour and continued walking without looking back. Aside from that event, we were almost always met with friendly smiles from the locals. But there were parts of the town that I wouldn't wander around in alone at night.

Later that evening, when we were at the poolside, we were approached by one of the hotel staff who told us in graphic detail about how bad things had actually been during the troubles. It was not uncommon to be accosted and bashed by a member of the local police force, or to be woken up at gunpoint in the small hours of the morning by a person demanding to know which way you were going to vote in the next election. In spite of all the troubles that had spanned the years 1998 to 2003, this staff member still regarded Harold Keke as a great man. As the Brothers we were about to examine were allegedly the victims of Keke's henchmen, I had some difficulty in seeing him as any kind of hero. We listened to what the local man had to say, but decided not to argue the toss about his allegiance to Harold Keke and his followers. It might have been an argument that we couldn't finish.


THE BROTHERS

The next morning it was back to the mortuary to begin examining the first of the seven slain Melanesian Brotherhood members. The story of the killing of the Brothers had been well documented in the local newspaper, the *Solomon Star*, and also in the newspapers back home, so I was familiar with the details of this tragic case. Six members of the GLF had confessed to their role in the killings, but would later plead not guilty to the crimes. This crime had rocked the nation and I was aware that our findings would be pivotal in the prosecution case. The ramifications could be huge.

As I fully expected that the remains would be in an advanced state of decomposition, I asked for a whiteboard to note down the injuries as I went. I also asked for a table and chair. RAMSI provided them within a few hours, so we were able to have the mortuary functioning at an optimal level before we examined the first body. Despite this, it was still fairly rudimentary. There were only several small buckets under the sink and the room could have done with a good cleanout. Caro attempted to clean the floor with a small broom before our first case and she later cleaned down the benches and shelves so that we could lay our instruments out on a reasonably clean surface.

The first body was brought into the mortuary and I opened the body bag. The remains were in an advanced state of decomposition, and, in many areas, bare bones were present. We photographed the whole body and then in one-thirds to document it from all angles. We then carefully removed and described the clothing and looked carefully for any signs of knife penetration or bullet wounds. I identified many areas of rib fracture, but no firm evidence of gunshot. These results agreed with the witness statements about the death of Brother Nathaniel Sado. This case took over two hours to conclude, but the procedure would provide a template for the others.

The Melanesian Brotherhood's clothing is very distinctive and well recognised in the community. They wear a black shirt, black shorts and a black and white sash tied at the waist. Many carry a staff or holy stick, considered by some locals to have magical powers. They almost always wear a distinctive oval bronze pendant, the badge of office of their religious order. Caro was somewhat unnerved by seeing these religious Brothers walking through the streets, as we had come to know the items of clothing intimately, even down to the distinctive clothing label. It brought the human face back to the work we were doing. These were not just decomposed bodies of forensic interest, but were once loved and revered members of the religious community of Honiara.

At the end of the autopsy, the floor was covered with dirty water, grit and mud and all the instruments needed to be cleaned, dried and put away for the following case. As we were to be in the Solomon Islands for the following eight days, we decided not to hurry, but to proceed in an orderly fashion, so as to perform each case to the best of our abilities. We therefore spent the remainder of the afternoon cleaning up and checking the supplies of the mortuary. It was amazing how much rubbish had accumulated on the shelves and in the cupboards over the preceding few years. Material that had absolutely no application in mortuary work had been placed there—out of sight, out of mind.

As we left the mortuary and headed down behind the main hospital building towards the beachfront, further surprises awaited us. Between the mortuary building and the beach lay approximately thirty to forty metres of partially grassed earth, punctuated by large areas of incinerator ash and hospital refuse. As we carefully walked through this morass of debris, we were horrified to see thousands of hypodermic needles, intravenous cannulae, lancets and small, broken glass ampoules scattered among the grass and ash. Local adults and children were walking casually through the debris in their bare feet. It would be so easy for one of these innocent people to tread on a needle infected by hepatitis C or worse.

Later, when I took off my gumboots before we returned to our lodgings, I would find a syringe needle had embedded itself in the sole of my right boot.

We found confidential medical records and many burnt and destroyed surgical instruments. There were large numbers of vaginal speculums and other instruments ranging from simple artery forceps to elaborate retractors, some quite sophisticated and expensive. The surgical staff were obviously not doing an instrument count at the end of each operation, but were simply wrapping up instruments in the surgical drapes covering the patient and throwing them away. It looked as though the hospital was losing about two to three instruments per week. In an impoverished third world country such as this, surgical instruments should be regarded as irreplaceable and treated as though they were solid gold.

We attempted to correct this by seeking an audience with key management personnel and we requested that the army be asked to cordon off the area, bulldoze the topsoil into piles and dig a large pit to dispose of the waste. This recommendation was not acted upon, but I was relieved to find on subsequent visits to the hospital that the area had been generally cleaned up. Empty 44-gallon drums and yellow sharps disposal containers had been provided to prevent the indiscriminate scattering of potentially dangerous and infectious material. At least this was a step in the right direction.

## FLYDAY

It was now 11 October, and we had already examined two of the seven slain Brothers. On this day, the body we were examining was more fleshy than the ones we had previously examined. I found evidence he had been bound at the wrists and shot through the chest. There was a single, neat bullet hole through the victim's shirt.

While we were performing the examinations, the geckos clung to the ceilings and walls, watching intently. Their intent was obvious—to feast on the gathering flies. We named them 'Harold Geke and Friends'. The smell of decomposition was attracting flies and within minutes, the air was thick with them. They were the size of raisins and packed a punch if they happened to hit you. On one occasion, a fly actually knocked my glasses off my face. Caro was too scared to open her mouth in case one flew down her throat. They just kept on coming and coming until the air was a black haze of thousands and thousands of flies.

It was impossible to continue the examination in these circumstances, and so we called a temporary halt to the procedure. We found a can of flyspray and emptied the entire contents into the room. We left the building to allow the flyspray to do its job and walked around to find the entry point. Sure enough, there was a large gap between the air-conditioner and the wall where the cardboard had rotted away. We could actually see the flies coming and going through this small gap. After about fifteen minutes, we went back to the post-mortem room and found the brown terracotta-tiled floor and benches completely covered with dead flies that crunched noisily underfoot. It took a while to sweep them away and clean up after the carnage so we could complete the autopsy. We called this 'Flyday', although it was actually Saturday.

The following morning, the team returned to the mortuary. We intended to perform a further two examinations and hoped for an early finish in the afternoon. But the mortuary had been left in a very dirty state from the activities of the day before, as the water pressure had failed us yet again. We spent the first half-hour sweeping the floor again and cleaning down the benches. Fortunately, the water supply returned later, although even on a good day the water pressure was little more than a dribble. It was certainly not strong enough to flush away debris on the floor. The best method was to tip full buckets of water onto the floor rather than use the hose that dangled from the sink. This was the worst problem, though, and in all other respects the mortuary, while basic, was quite serviceable.

Once everything was in order, we began the examination of the first body for the day. It was in an advanced state of decomposition, but in spite of this I was able to determine that the deceased had suffered blunt force trauma to the back. The area of decomposed tissue still showed obvious areas of bruising into the deeper layers. It was very likely that this man had been bashed at some time. I identified a bullet hole in his shirt, but there was no apparent exit or entry wound. The bullet must have passed through the body without inflicting skeletal injury. Examination of the bones of the left forearm, however, showed a definite bullet defect through the ulna. This man had been shot in the arm at least once, but we could not determine whether it was a defence wound or whether the bullet had passed through some other victim before hitting his arm. This tallied with witness statements that one of the victims had been shot in the arm before death.

We began the second case in the afternoon. It showed changes very similar to the ones we had already seen. This case yielded for the first time definitive ballistic evidence. A bullet was firmly lodged in the spine and I was able to extract it and keep it for the police as prime evidence.

Members of RAMSI generally provided lunch. Given advance notice, we could secure hot packs from the GBR kitchen. We had lunch under the shade of a covered walkway immediately next to the mortuary to shield us from both the searing sun and the intermittent monsoonal rains in the afternoons. On this particular afternoon, a member of the Australian Protective Services (APS) sat down with us on the edge of a concrete drain beside the hospital building. He had inadvertently sat in a pool of wet, white paint. When he got up for a smoke, there were howls of laughter and calls of, 'Hey, white-arse!' from the group. Any excuse for a laugh was welcome.

We started early again on the following day, Monday 13 October. As a legacy of the previous day's work, the drain immediately beneath the mortuary table had become blocked. We hadn't realised that a plunger on a long rod for clearing the drain was kept behind the fridge, so we had poured the accumulated water containing grit, mud and the products of decomposition into several large, plastic bins. Overnight, with temperatures still in the high twenties, they had become fermentation tanks. On opening the mortuary doors that morning, we were greeted with a blast of foul gas that had accumulated during the night and could see bubbles forming on the surface of the bins. We managed to unblock the drain and emptied the bins. This gross and offensive material was then able to run free into the drain over the next few minutes.

Although Caro and I were hardened to horrendous sights and smells from many years of forensic experience, we gagged through this process. Caro quietly asked the RAMSI observer in the mortuary whether she could have a moment of privacy and, as he left, lost her breakfast down the drain. When John found out about it, he awarded her his plastic 'Winner Medal' for gallant service while we were having dinner at a Chinese restaurant. The medal had travelled with John from Australia to Cyprus on a mission in 2000 and then back to Australia and on to the Solomon Islands. It was quite an honour for Caro to be presented with it and she accepted the award graciously.

The following day, we concluded the remaining cases. I identified a repeating pattern in the remaining two bodies, a combination of rib fracture and gunshot. In the last body examined, I found a small sliver of silver metal within the tissues of the chest. The religious pendant was separate in the body bag. Once we put the string back around the neck, I realised that the bullet had passed through the toggle of the pendant before entering through the chest, passing downwards and ultimately lodging in the spine.

At the end of each autopsy, I sat at the desk and filled in an interim post-mortem report on the pro-forma that I had brought with me. I would dictate the reports back home and return them to the Solomon Islands with a turnaround time of approximately two weeks. Although the mission was in essence an uncomplicated one, its results would form the basis of a powerful prosecution case against Ronnie Cawa and his henchmen.

Our final day of work at the mortuary was on Tuesday 14 October. We were joined at the mortuary by the porter and the hospital's infection control officer. Together, we scrubbed the walls, the tiles, the floor and the door with disinfectant. It was probably the first time in a good while that the mortuary had undergone such a thorough cleaning, and it was long overdue. As a parting legacy, we donated scalpel blades, aprons, our surgical scrubs, a pair of safety glasses, disinfectant and sharps containers. After a solid morning's work, the mortuary looked quite reasonable. When I returned early the following year, I was heartened to find the mortuary had remained quite clean and tidy. The staff now took pride in the small facility and no longer saw it as a place to be avoided.

## NATIONAL DAY OF MOURNING

We spent our last evening at the Mendana poolside, as usual. There were spectacular thunderstorms and we enjoyed the free light show and swimming under heavy monsoon rain. The thunderstorms in the Solomon Islands are spectacular and rival those I've seen in Darwin.

The seven fallen Brothers were remembered in a moving service conducted on Saturday 24 April 2004. They were buried at the Mother House of the Melanesian Brothers at Tabalia, at the western edge of the island. The day of the funerals was declared a national day of mourning. Thousands lined the roads to witness their final farewell and burial, which was also attended by the Governor General, the Prime Minister, other ministers and the Papua New Guinea High Commission.

I would return to the Solomon Islands in July 2005 to provide expert forensic evidence in the trial of Ronnie Cawa, Joses Kejoa, Owen Isa and 'K' for the slaying of six of the missionaries. Brother Nathaniel Sado's case was due to be heard early the following year. Though the accused men claimed that they were defending themselves against the brothers' holy sticks, in October 2005 Cawa, Isa and Kejoa were all found guilty of killing the brothers and sentenced to life imprisonment.

# EIGHT

# SOLOMON ISLANDS
## JANUARY 2004

In late December 2003, the forensic and investigation arm of the Regional Assistance Mission to Solomon Islands (RAMSI) had been busy and there were plans to mount a further round of exhumations and autopsies. In early January, John McIntyre called me to see whether I would be available to spend a further two weeks in Honiara from 15 to 30 January. There were three operations running where bodies needed to be exhumed and examined. There were also two other bodies from specific cases. These investigations were being led by John and two other detective inspectors. John was managing the exhumation operation to make sure that sufficient evidence would be gained to assess the individual cases. He also negotiated with Australia and New Zealand to get two Disaster Victim Identification (DVI) personnel from each country to come over and assist. A New Zealand Police (NZPOL) inspector was already working with John and he managed to second him for the two weeks it was expected to take.

Two weeks would be plenty of time to examine the two fresh

bodies currently awaiting examination and the further ten scheduled for exhumation. I agreed immediately and went to see if Caro was available to join me again on this mission. Unfortunately, the Christmas and New Year holidays and the demands of the staff roster meant that it was impossible for any forensic technical staff to be released. We were both disappointed. I had to look further afield to find someone who was up to the demands of the job.

ENTER THE ENTOMOLOGIST

I needed a forensic technician who would be totally at ease with the handling of grossly decomposed and maggot-infested bodies, as well as skeletal remains. I immediately thought of Mel. Dr Melanie Archer is a zoologist by training and had recently gained her PhD in forensic entomology. Her fieldwork on the rate of decay using pig carcasses and estimation of the time since death is groundbreaking. She is one of the very few forensic entomologists nationwide and the only one to practise in the state of Victoria, as the Consultant Forensic Entomologist to the Victorian Institute of Forensic Medicine (VIFM).

I'd known Mel for some time and had enlisted her expertise on problematic cases of my own on several occasions. She is one of the most intelligent, articulate and hardworking people I have ever met and had the pleasure to work with. She also has an industrial strength vocabulary and for this reason, wears the tag of 'Dr Potty Mouth' with pride. She was just the person I was looking for. Happily, she leapt at the chance to accompany me and over the next few days we revised the equipment list that Caro and I had put together for the previous two missions.

We headed off to Tullamarine airport for our seven o'clock flight. We had arranged with the Australian Federal Police (AFP) to purchase duty-free goods in advance, as, although we were heading overseas, we were departing from a domestic terminal. It pays to think ahead in these circumstances. After making our purchases, we made our way to the departure lounge and presented our boarding passes. To my shocked surprise, they were rejected by the scanner. What could possibly have gone wrong? As I was contemplating the disastrous scenarios that could have prevented us from even getting as far as first base, the flight attendant told us that we had been upgraded to business class. Caro's friend at Qantas had waved her magic wand again.

The flight over was comfortable and uneventful and six hours later we touched down in Honiara. As usual, the heat and humidity were oppressive and the small customs and immigration area at the airport was suffocating. We were met by John McIntyre and several of his colleagues. It was great to see John again and he was not surprised to see us clutching the now familiar bright orange and green duty-free bags. After introductions all around, John drove us to the Mendana Hotel. Despite the gruelling nature of my work, particularly on war crimes investigations, I think that the main reason I am able to cope with it and even thrive on it is largely due to the fantastic people I have worked with.

As we drove to the hotel, I was pleased to see that Honiara had changed for the better since I'd last been there. The RAMSI intervention had done much to restore law and order in the town. Many more shops had opened, and the locals were peacefully going about their day-to-day activities. The streets were cleaner, with much less litter, and even the distinctive blood-red betel nut staining that had covered the pavements had been cleaned up. I was glad to be part of the team that was helping to restore peace to the traumatised citizens of this country.

## MENDANA

When we checked into the Mendana Hotel, we were given the keys to our rooms, which for some reason were on opposite sides of the building. I had warned Mel to be prepared for the quirks and idiosyncrasies of the hotel. The accommodation is average, with a comfortable bed and ample bathroom. The functioning of the air-conditioner, television and refrigerator fluctuates with the intermittent power supply. In addition, the hotel seems to be on a continual steep learning curve in terms of service and facilities. The furniture comes apart in your hands if you attempt to shift anything and meal deliveries are unpredictable at best. But it was the towels that I found the most difficult. A long hot shower at the end of the day's work at the mortuary is an absolute must and the towels were removed in the morning and not replaced until mid to late afternoon.

These minor inconveniences were vastly outweighed by the charm of the staff. This was my third stay at the hotel and I was greeted as an old friend. The people of the Solomon Islands are very friendly and welcoming; even the laundry and housekeeping women recognised me and welcomed me fondly. It set the tone for our stay and I could tell that it was going to be a good mission.

After we had unpacked and settled in, we had the rest of the afternoon free. I gave Mel a quick tour of Honiara. We walked up the main street and looked at the many souvenir shops and cafes that we would later come to know well. This was easily accomplished in under two hours. Mel relished her first experience of cold coconut milk out of the shell for two Solomons dollars (approximately fifty cents Australian). After this, we walked around the harbour and looked at the ruste-out ferries.

The beach in front of the Mendana was delightful as always.

Two Solomon Islands navy patrol boats were anchored nearby. They were numbered 03 and 04. Apparently, they had originally been numbered 01 and 02, but to the locals the number 01 refers to the wife and the number 02 refers to the mistress. To avoid embarrassment, the boats' numbers were changed. Although they are anchored at a secured harbour, we managed to talk our way through the security gate and had a close look at 04, which is named the *Lata*. Members of RAMSI had told us that during the recent conflict a militia group had commandeered the *Lata* and had opened fire on villagers with a 50-calibre Browning machine gun. Fortunately nobody had been injured. Upon close inspection, we could see multiple bullet indentations on the wheel housing, a legacy of the recapture of the *Lata*. This brought home to us the ferocity and complexity of the turmoil raging in Guadalcanal in the years 1998 to 2003.

The following day, John drove us to the American war memorial, which overlooks the capital. It was erected in honour of the Americans and allies who lost their lives during the Guadalcanal campaign of the Second World War. This magnificent monument consists of a seven-metre-high pylon and four walls pointing to the four major battle areas upon which are inscribed the names of the battleships, destroyers, aircraft, and land-based battalions that suffered enormous losses during the August 1942 to February 1943 campaign. We then drove for about twenty minutes east of Honiara to visit the Japanese war memorial, which Caro and I had visited on our last trip. At the time of our first visit, the tall, white pillars had been completely obliterated with extremely offensive graffiti. Much of it was aimed towards the Australian intervention, specifically RAMSI. When Mel and I visited, the monument had been repainted and restored in preparation for a Japanese delegation that was visiting Honiara at that time.

## THE FIRST CASES

The following morning, John and some others picked us up and took us to the mortuary at the National Referral Hospital at Honiara. I was eager to show Mel the mortuary, as I had shown her photographs after the second mission and had told her about the improvements we had been working on. I was relieved to see that apart from a small amount of litter on the floor and some dust on the benches the mortuary had been kept in a good state of repair. We unpacked our instruments, scrubs, gloves and aprons and brought out the invaluable table, chair and whiteboard from storage. The whiteboard would be indispensable on this mission, as well as the following one in May.

The mortuary does not need to be an unhappy place. At home at the VIFM we frequently have the radio on softly in the background as we perform the post-mortems. Mel and I thought it would be a good idea to have some music in the mortuary at Honiara, so Mel brought along a CD player and I supplied the small speakers. We are both aficionados of the Norwegian death punk band Turbonegro. After the first few songs, John described it as 'young, angry music'. The facial expressions on the others in the room as they turned to John showed their thoughts—could he do anything to stop it? The following morning, John brought along his contribution. Allegedly, John and one of his colleagues Brian Dobrich ('Dobbo') used to pump themselves up in the morning by listening to the UK-based Hindi rock band Cornershop. Mel and I listened to 'Brimful of Asha' and, as one, reciprocated with the same expressions on our faces.

We were ready to start the first case of the day and laid out on the post-mortem table the tiny body of a small baby. The details of the case were sketchy. John's information was that the baby was thought to be about four hours old at the time of death. The body was found in a shallow grave with its head slightly protruding from the soil. The mother had initially denied the birth and then later claimed that the child was stillborn. The aim of the autopsy was to establish the gestation of the baby and to see whether it had drawn breath after birth. The baby had been frozen before my examination and had thawed out during the morning. As a result of the external examination, I concluded that the child was almost certainly less than term. I estimated that it was more likely to be about thirty-four weeks gestation rather than forty weeks. I couldn't determine whether the child had been alive at birth because decomposition had already set in. The normal procedure was to establish buoyancy of the lungs and thoracic organs to dem-onstrate that air had entered the lungs. As the process of decompo-sition had distended the lungs with gases, I was unable to give an opinion on whether or not this child had been born alive. It was an unsatisfactory end, but not an uncommon one in normal forensic practice.

We turned our attention to the second case of the day. We had inspected the body at the beginning of the morning, but it had been too frozen to proceed, so we had placed it back into its metal casket and left it out in the sun to thaw while we completed the autopsy on the baby. Once again, John outlined what was known of the events surrounding the death. This time, the victim was a woman in her fifties who had allegedly been beaten by her son-in-law during a domestic argument. It was thought that the son-in-law may have kicked the woman in the side of the body, between the ribs and the hip, and that she had died as a result of this some time later. I examined the body of the woman closely. I could see no sign of any bruising or abrasions, certainly nothing to substantiate a forceful kick to the abdomen. John suggested that perhaps the woman had died of natural causes, such as a heart attack.

As soon as I began the internal examination, the cause of death became immediately apparent. I found about a litre and a half of partially frozen liquid and clotted blood within the abdominal cavity. The blood was present because of a ruptured spleen. Malarial infection had almost certainly caused the spleen to be enlarged, a common finding in the Solomon Islands. I thought it likely that the spleen had ruptured as a result of a kick to the abdomen and that the woman had then died of cardiogenic shock some time later. The following year, I would return to the Solomon Islands to give evidence to this effect. The accused was ultimately sentenced to life imprisonment for first-degree murder. An appeal is pending.

The time now came to reconstruct this body. Mel had never reconstructed a fresh body, but before we left for Honiara our mortuary technicians had shown her the rudimentary skills. Despite her lack of experience, she managed to do a sterling job. For her, it was see one, do one. This skill would become all the more important on the following mission where we were confronted with several fresh bodies to examine. Our working day was over once we had completed these two cases and we packed everything away and returned to the hotel.

There were a large number of restaurants close by and over the course of the next couple of weeks we would visit many of them. After a meal, we would usually sit together in one of our hotel rooms chatting and sipping away on our duty free booty. We could watch BBC television, ABC Asia Pacific and several stations catering for Japanese tourists. It was soon obvious that the BBC news was on a virtual continuous loop and that the ABC channel was variable in its content at best. We had a great time watching the Japanese channels, though. Many of the advertisements were hilarious and we were often left wondering what the product being advertised actually was. To this day, we still don't know what Le Sort is. Mel became quite addicted to the sumo wrestling, which I could only tolerate in very small doses.

Over the next three days, we examined six exhumed bodies. Most of them came from the beach at Pite, which seemed to be an unhappy dumping ground for many of the victims of the violence. Many of the Missionary Brothers had been buried there, and we would visit this site again in May. These bodies ranged in their degree of decomposition from quite fleshy to almost entirely skeletonised, so we had to vary the procedure for each case. Before long, we had established what had become, for me at least, a fairly familiar routine. Where the bodies were more or less complete, although grossly decomposed, I performed a conventional autopsy. In the cases where the bodies were almost entirely skeletonised, we separated the bones from the soft tissues, washed them, laid them out on a mobile table we had found outside the mortuary and examined them meticulously for signs of injury. The viciousness of the conflict was reflected in the range of injuries we encountered. They included gunshot wounds, blunt force trauma to the head and chest and, in one case, a knife wound. In many cases, there was a combination of both gunshot and blunt force trauma.

At the conclusion of each autopsy, we retrieved one of the femurs and measured it to estimate the height of the individual. We also extracted several teeth for DNA analysis. Once this final step was concluded, we placed the bones back in the body bag to be returned to their families. Each autopsy took one to one and a half hours to perform. As we had ten decomposed bodies to examine, we brought them out of the refrigerated container in a step-wise fashion. We very quickly got an efficient system in place and were able to average two to three cases per day.

As a zoologist, Mel was fascinated by the behaviour of the geckos as they watched us closely, making the most of the occasion by feasting on the blowflies that were attracted by the decomposing bodies. Having already witnessed one incident of cannibalism, Mel threw a pen at an adult gecko as it was about to eat one of its tiny young. We found the pen the following year behind one of the high shelves. Occasionally there would be a gecko fight. Two geckos would face-off each other, wave their tails from side to side and the first to back down would quickly scurry back to a position of safety, leaving the winner triumphant.

## CHOPPER TIME

I had asked John whether we would be able to attend an exhumation. I wanted Mel to experience all the dimensions of third-world pathology and the helicopter trip is a bonus—an enjoyable 'big toy'. John somehow managed to secure us two seats on a Bell Huey helicopter due to leave Honiara the following morning for an exhumation on the Weathercoast. This was a designated rest day, but we leapt at the chance to travel by helicopter to work in the field. He picked us up bright and early the following morning. We headed to Guadalcanal Beach Resort (GBR) for an early breakfast and a briefing session, and then headed off for the five-minute drive to Henderson Airport.

We congregated at Air Point of Departure (APOD) near the main runway. While we waited, we wandered over to one of the tents containing a small shop selling soft drinks, chips, chocolate bars, Australian newspapers and RAMSI merchandise. The RAMSI emblem is a blue and green disc with the dove of peace superimposed upon it. Scattered across this emblem are light green blotches representing the Solomon Islands group. Mel picked up a stubbie holder with this emblem on it and asked in all innocence, 'What's with the bird shit?' I replied, 'That's the Solomons, man!' The symbolism of the emblem had completely escaped her.

Two Bell Huey helicopters sat on the airfield. The pilot and co-pilot met us and gave us brief instructions on safety procedures. The last instruction given to us by the pilot was '… and don't touch my knife!' He had a large-bladed knife strapped to the back of the seat in the cockpit, presumably so he could cut himself free of the safety harness should disaster strike. John had organised for Mel and me to sit on the side seats of the helicopter rather than the usual position behind the pilot and co-pilot. We strapped ourselves in as the slide doors of the Bell Huey were pushed forward and back. We were facing directly outwards with nothing more than a running board beneath our feet. Within moments, the rotor blades roared into life and the helicopter ran along the length of the runway before lifting off. It was exhilarating to feel the air blasting through the cabin, blowing our hair in all directions. We leaned over and watched the dense jungle, mountain ridges and deep ravines passing by beneath us.

The helicopter was headed for the village of Mbambanakira (generally referred to as Bam Bam), just a few minutes from the beach of the Weathercoast. We were to stop here to pick up the members of the exhumation team who had stayed overnight. The helicopter landed on a soccer field in the village, which contained grass huts, wooden buildings, schools and a small health centre. The airstrip was within walking distance of the village. We picked up the team, and then the convoy headed off to Chelu on the Weathercoast.

The helicopter flew above the brilliant blue-green water, and long stretches of white beach sand abutting incredibly dense jungle. Before long, a large ravine opened up before us. The helicopter turned and flew down into the valley and dropped us off next to a creek bed. The creek was running slowly at this time of year, but the high bed of gravel rising several metres on either side of it indicated the depth it must reach during the monsoon season. The other helicopters landed and everybody hopped out onto the creek bed and unloaded the gear.

Unlike the first two missions, where members of RAMSI exhumed the bodies, these were to be exhumed by a dedicated team led by Federal Agent Mick Travers, who headed up the DVI arm of the AFP. John McIntyre and several other RAMSI members, Mel and I and the exhumation team then set off for the dig site which was about one kilometre upstream. Several members carried the heavy metal coffin we had brought with us along the creek bed. Although the water was less than half a metre deep, the current was surprisingly strong and the creek bed was lined with slippery round boulders. At one point, I lost my footing and slipped, landing on my right knee. My main concern was that if I managed to injure myself again, I would never live it down. Fortunately John hadn't noticed this slip and I suffered no more than a slight bruise to the knee and a good soaking.

After half an hour or so, we reached the cliff that we would have to climb to reach the gravesite. The cliff rose steeply from the creek bed on a deeply forested gradient lined with slippery brown mud. We scrambled up one at a time, clutching onto vines and branches and anything else that we could grab onto. Finally, we all made it to the top and started out for the gravesite, which was only a short distance away. We knew we had reached the spot where the body lay when we saw a simple cross etched into one of the trees.

We were told that it had been reported that this man was marched here at gunpoint and was then allegedly shot in the head with a .22 calibre rifle. It had also been reported that he might have been shot in the buttocks during the course of his final journey. The grave was an old one and we fully expected that only a skeleton would remain. We were about to begin when Mel raised a few eyebrows by pulling out her bug-catching net to collect some of the insects that were flying all around the place. John later remarked to me that after all the stuff they had seen so far, he and the other team members found it truly bizarre that someone was out here leaping about trying to catch blowflies.

After half an hour of carefully paring back the rich, loamy soil of the floor of the jungle, the first bone was exposed. I could tell that it was an ankle, and I was able to guide the direction of the digging towards the head. Before long, the entire skeleton was exposed. The bones were exceedingly dry and brittle. Much of the calcium had been leached away by the tannic acid formed by rotting vegetation. Many of the small bones could not be identified at all. One of the team members uncovered the skull. He was unsure whether it was in fact the skull, as he thought it looked like a coconut. He decided to tap it with his spade to check. What happened next appeared to play out in slow motion. As we watched in horror, the skull shattered under the impact of the spade. We could not believe what we had just seen. John hadn't witnessed this and when I told him what had happened, he said, 'Yeah, right, a coconut with teeth.' To say that he was less than impressed would be a serious understatement.

We carefully gathered all the skull fragments and bones and placed them into a body bag. We took them back down the slope into the ravine and placed them into the casket that was waiting there. One of the team had rigged up a nylon rope from the top to the bottom of the slope so we could abseil down. The descent took no time at all compared to the struggle we had on the way up. Then began the journey back to the point where the helicopter would pick us up. The weight of the coffin had not changed greatly, as the skeleton weighed no more than a few kilograms.

Once we had reached the pickup point, we set our gear aside and ate the light lunch that we had packed. We were then informed by radio contact that the helicopter would not be back for an hour or so, so a few of us had a dip in the fast running, cold waters of the creek. Before long, we heard the thud, thud, thud of the helicopters in the distance. Within moments, a single-engine Huey New Zealand army helicopter and a double-engine Huey Hevi Lift both came out of the sky above us. The Hevi Lift is a larger craft used for the transportation of equipment and personnel. On the way back to Honiara, we marvelled at the dense, almost impenetrable jungle under the setting sun. The whole area seemed almost uninhabited. You could hide a million bodies out here and nobody would ever know. About ten minutes into the flight, fatigue set in. To Mel's amazement, I managed to have a nanna-nap during our return journey. She confided to me later that she wondered whether I might have had a quiet coronary during the flight, but wasn't sure what to do if I had. Before long, the helicopter landed back at APOD and the casket was removed and transferred to Honiara Hospital for the autopsy the following morning.

As the equipment was being stored away, Mel and I decided to explore the grassy area of the landing strip and, to our great surprise and delight, we discovered many large, black rhinoceros beetles. The beetles had all died, probably as a result of insecticides sprayed in an attempt to quell the mosquitoes responsible for malaria in this area. Mel was like a kid in a lolly shop. Within moments, we had filled our caps to overflowing with large museum quality specimens. When we got back to the hotel that evening, she delighted in examining each insect closely. She separated the best ones for her collection, many of which she would submit to the

Museum of Victoria's large entomological archive. She then meticulously pinned the insects into a carrying case, noting the time, date and location of their discovery. She was in her element.

## THE CHELU CASE

The next morning, we examined the body we had exhumed from Chelu following the usual procedure. It took very little time to wash the bones and set them aside. There were no items of clothing, blindfolds or ligatures present. I assessed the man's height from the length of the femur and made a rough assessment of his age, but that was about it. Thankfully, enough of the larger parts of the cranium had survived the assault with the shovel at the dig site for me to reassemble the skull. Once that was done, I could see an incomplete hole six millimetres in diameter through the right side of the skull. This hole had all the hallmarks of a bullet hole. When I examined the pelvic bones, I was able to find a similar but larger defect through the right side of the pelvis. These findings were consistent with the circumstances of the case as we knew them at the time. I wrote up a provisional report and we packed the bones back into the body bag and returned it to the refrigerated container until the remains could be returned to the family.

John's organisational skills were admirable. During our stay in the Solomon Islands, it was very easy to forget what day it was. If I asked John whether it was Monday or Tuesday, he would reply that it was day five of the mission. That didn't help much. John had placed a large and detailed flow chart on the side of the refrigerator in the mortuary. Unfortunately, overnight the paper had sagged under the weight of condensation from the metal surface and now it drooped sadly onto the mortuary floor. Initially crestfallen, he later came around as the rest of us couldn't contain ourselves.

We had the following day off, so, on the suggestion of one

of the New Zealand exhumation team members, we set off for Bonegi Beach to do a bit of snorkelling. This spot is just to the west of Honiara and an easy half-hour drive over sealed roads. It was a popular diving spot, as a large Japanese freighter had been sunk there during the Second World War and its funnel protruded above the water line at low tide. Apparently, an American fighter aircraft had managed to drop a bomb down the funnel and the freighter had sunk where it was hit. The wreckage of a Japanese landing craft also lay on the beach nearby. We put on our snorkelling gear and swam in the warm clear water to the wreck. I was surprised to see that the boat was quite well preserved. We swam from bow to stern looking down into the large, cavernous cargo holds and marvelling at the myriad of brightly coloured fish and bright purple sea anemone. It was very relaxing and we felt rejuvenated and ready for the next few days, which we knew were going to be pretty full on.

## NAKUA AND TITINGE

The next day, we examined two more exhumed victims from Nakua village who had been shot. We were able to complete the autopsies of these skeletonised remains quickly. I managed to recover the small conical brass-jacketed projectile tip from the remains of one of the men. Due to the advanced state of decomposition, I was not able to confidently say where the bullet had entered. I could tell from the pattern of fractured ribs and a shaved defect on one of the right ribs that this man had been bashed and stabbed as well as shot. In my experience in the Solomon Islands thus far, this was a unique case.

The following day we headed off to Titinge, a small village to the west of Honiara. The road, while sealed for the most part, is punctuated by deep potholes near Rove. We drove past the Rove Police Station, which incorporates the prison in which Harold

Keke, Ronnie Cawa and others are now held following their conviction for murder in the High Court in February of 2005. It is a bleak-looking place, consisting of a few tin sheds standing in the full blazing sun, and surrounded by a high cyclone fence with razor wire. It would not be a pleasant place to spend the rest of your life. We drove a bit further and bare, grassed ridges emerged from the jungle, much as Uluru does from the desert. We turned a hard left towards the ridge where the village of Titinge is located.

The man we were about to exhume had been buried in a coffin in the local cemetery. According to witness statements, he had been struck by a vehicle and then shot. The DVI team assembled and located the gravesite, hard against the edge of the cemetery with a steep slope immediately behind it. They erected a tent-like structure over the gravesite to protect the diggers from the intense sun. Mel had brought her entomology gear, and busied herself by stalking insects in the tall grass. After an hour or so of heavy digging in the heavily compacted soil, we heard the familiar dull thud as the shovel hit the coffin lid. It was about two metres down. The coffin was huge, and because it was buried so deep and next to the steep slope, we had very little room to manoeuvre. We attempted to haul it up using a makeshift block and tackle, but it was just too heavy. We decided that the most practical way around this problem was to break the coffin lid open and remove the body only, rather than the entire coffin. We were pleasantly surprised to see that the body had been enclosed in an intact, zippered, blue body bag. But the entire body had effectively liquefied within the bag and the smell was overwhelming. Although the body bag had been encased in a second bag, a foul smelling fluid leaked out as we dragged it up the embankment to the waiting metal casket.

LIQUID MAN

The body was transferred to the mortuary, and we began the autopsy examination early that afternoon. John McIntyre attended the autopsy as the manager of exhumations, along with a member of RAMSI and one from the Royal Solomon Islands Police (RSIP). To this day, we still reminisce about the unusual condition of the body and the lucky find at the end of the examination. The mortuary room is barely large enough to contain the pathologist, technician and the required number of photographers and observers. We were all squashed in together, and when we opened the body bag, an overpowering blast of pure ammonia filled the room. A fine, white, misty cloud emanated from the bag causing everyone to recoil and rub their stinging eyes. I had never encountered a body in this state before or since. Perhaps because it had been completely wrapped in two body bags, the body had undergone a form of complete liquefactive decomposition. Virtually all of the tissue had turned into an opaque, bubbling, soupy mass. The bones protruded from the morass of decomposition fluid. They were gleaming white because they had been chemically cleaned as the protein in the body converted to ammonia. We had to break every fifteen minutes or so to get a breath of fresh air, so the autopsy took a long time.

As the bones were washed and laid out, catastrophic injury involving the area of the pelvis became apparent. In a separate injury, the left pelvic bone and hip joint had been shattered, consistent with the statements that the man had been struck by a vehicle before being shot. I was able to identify the impact point of a bullet on the inside surface of the left side of the pelvis. I thought it likely that it had passed through the right flank, impacted on the pelvic bone and rebounded inwardly. This meant that the bullet must still be there among all of this liquid.

As the implications of this dawned on me, I asked John whether he could possibly get hold of a quarter-inch sieve. Within half an hour we had one and Mel and I scooped up the thick, soupy material that filled the body bag and poured it into several buckets. I would guess that there was in excess of thirty litres in total. Slowly but surely, we poured the entire liquid contents of this unfortunate individual through the sieve. It seemed like such an undignified way to treat someone who had already been murdered, but it was crucial that we retrieve the ballistic evidence. Small amounts of fleshy material still remained in the liquid, so I had to press this material against the sieve with my gloved fingers to check for anything solid. As we were processing the second last bucket, and I was beginning to lose hope, I felt something firm and sharp against my fingers. Sure enough, I'd found the jacketing of the bullet, which was a typical high velocity metal jacket round used by the militia. John couldn't believe it, and was delighted that we had managed to retrieve the projectile against all odds. It proved to be the very best evidence of all.

We wrapped up the remains of the body for its return to the family. I must say that I was very glad to finish that particular case and hoped I would never encounter anything similar again. All our clothing and equipment had absorbed the smell of the remains of this poor individual and our first priority was to get back to the hotel as soon as possible for serious cleaning. We ran to our rooms for the eagerly anticipated warm shower. But the power supply had failed, resulting in zero water pressure. In these extreme circumstances, we decided that we would have to use the swimming pool. We figured from a cold, hard, scientific point of view that the dilution factor and the chlorine would take care of any nasties that may have been on our skin.

## THE LAST SAD CASE

On the morning of 26 January, four days before our departure, an unexpected case materialised. As I was there, I was asked to perform the examination. The body of an eighteen-month-old boy, who had died two days previously, was brought to the mortuary. I was told that it was possible that the child, who had been involved in a custody dispute, had died under suspicious circumstances. I could see no suspicious marks on the little body, certainly nothing to indicate physical abuse. The internal examination was unremarkable. A similar case was presented to me in East Timor. I discussed the case with the investigating team and told them that the only way to resolve this case would be to take extensive specimens for toxicological analysis and send them back to Australia for further testing. I collected and preserved samples of the relevant body fluids and organs, which were transported to Canberra for analysis. Mel reconstructed the small body, a task which was made all the more difficult by having to do it neatly, so as not to add to the distress of the relatives.

I would receive the toxicological results in May 2004. The sample of blood contained forty milligrams per litre of Chloroquine, an anti-malarial medication. This level, especially for one so young, is a lethal dose. This matter is yet to be resolved; the lethal dose could either have been ingested accidentally, or forcefully administered.

## AUSTRALIA DAY

Australia Day was looming. John kindly asked Mel and me whether we would like to come to the celebrations at GBR. We are not by nature party animals, but thought it would be an interesting sociological observation to attend later in the afternoon. We were not disappointed. We arrived at GBR at about six thirty and activities were well underway. As the sun was going down and the Sol Brew was flowing, there were the inevitable punch-ups and arguments among some soldiers and international RAMSI police officers. Nothing nasty, but given the social constraints, pressures and isolation of this community, not unexpected.

One female army member launched herself off the sun deck in an attempt to jump into the swimming pool, but slipped at the last moment and crashed heavily and dangerously over a rubbish bin. We all feared for her immediate safety and, from my medical experience, I wouldn't have been surprised if she had been rendered a paraplegic. But she picked herself up, dusted herself off and had a laugh about it! The order was given—no more jumping off the decking into the swimming pool would be tolerated!

As the evening wore on, we met many very interesting people and somehow got caught up in the celebrations. A senior ranking RAMSI member picked Mel up and held her above his head while standing on the edge of the swimming pool. I thought he was only messing about with her and wouldn't actually throw her in. But as he tilted fifteen degrees off the vertical, I realised that the situation was going to reach its inevitable conclusion. They both fell into the swimming pool with a great splash. The next thing I heard was, 'Get the doc, Get the doc!' I had barely enough time to remove my glasses and stow my camera before I too found myself in the swimming pool with Mel, other RAMSI members, several floating plastic outdoor chairs and other flotsam and jetsam that had accumulated over the afternoon.

Fortunately, the pool water had been cleaned since our first visit to the base and it was a welcome relief to the still high temperatures and intense humidity of the evening. As the evening wore on, we decided to head back to the Mendana. John was kind enough to organise a lift for us. We headed back to the hotel, dripping wet in the back of a troop vehicle singing 'We're going home in the back of a divvie van!' It was a great end to a fun evening. The Australia Day of 2004 would contrast very starkly with the sombre marking of the day in 2005 after the tragic shooting of Adam Dunning in December 2004.

HOME AGAIN

On our last days in Honiara, Mel and I again roamed the streets checking out the shops and having the occasional drink of cold coconut milk straight from the shell. We took in the Cultural Museum, which had an impressive collection of ancient relics. Our scheduled return flight was due to leave Honiara on Friday 30 January at four thirty. We said goodbye to John and the team and boarded the plane and before long found ourselves home in Melbourne. Mel exclaimed that this was the highlight of her career thus far, but little did she know that the best was still to come. We were to return in May to perform many more cases and to experience the fun of more 'big toys'.

# NINE

# SOLOMON ISLANDS
## MAY 2004

After the completion of our tour in January, there had been rumours that a further mission might be mounted later in the year. During April and May, I received many communications from Federal Agent Mick Travers, with whom we had worked in January. This was to be a big mission. Mick told me that we would have two weeks to exhume twenty-two bodies from eight gravesites, the majority of which were located on the Weathercoast. Mick would again coordinate the Disaster Victim Identification (DVI) team, and again would enlist members of the New Zealand Police (NZPOL) to assist. Superintendent Harry Hains of the Australian Federal Police (AFP) would act as chief of operations and operation commander. Mel and I had met Harry during the exhumation at Titinge in January and we had all worked well together as a team. Harry is good to have around. He has a wicked sense of humour and nothing seems to ruffle his feathers. Happily, Mel was again able to accompany me as my forensic technician. It hadn't been that long since our last mission, so it took no time to repack the equipment we would require in the field and at the mortuary. The only downside to this mission was that our old friend John McIntyre had returned to Canberra to resume his normal duties. It would not be the same without him.

Mel and I were relieved to see that this time around our departure time from Tullamarine was to be five past one in the afternoon on 4 May. On our way to the airport I told Mel that this would be a busy mission with up to twenty-two bodies to be exhumed, meaning that we would have to conduct autopsies at a rate of three to four a day in addition to the field exhumation trips. There would be little time for rest and recreation, but we both knew that we were not going for a holiday. This was serious business. The flight to Brisbane passed quickly. Mick and his DVI team met us at the airport and a bus picked up the assembled team and took us to Amberley Air Force Base.

The exhumation and forensic team consisted of me as forensic pathologist, Mel as my forensic technician and eight members of the AFP and NZPOL. We had met several of the New Zealand members during the mission in January. On this occasion, an anthropologist had joined the team. Kate Oakley was to help us at the exhumation sites. We were happy to have the additional expertise on the team. This was to be a steep learning curve for Kate, as her anthropological training was largely animal based. She was eager to participate in the exhumation of human remains to expand her knowledge and also to observe the post-mortem procedure.

We reached Amberley Airforce Base, and after being delayed for some time at the security gate, we were finally allowed to enter. We were due to depart early the next morning and so planned to retire for an early night. After our rooms were allocated, we headed off for the dining room and had a good meal. From time to time we heard the thunderous sound of jets roaring overhead. The sound was irresistible. Mel and I quickly made our way to the airfield to watch these incredible machines take off and land. By this time, the night had settled in and the sky was black and clear. We made our way through the maze of buildings towards the tarmac. A large cyclone fence enclosed the tarmac area. We found a comfortable spot to sit and watched the jets coming and going for the next few hours. We observed fifteen take-offs and thirteen landings from our vantage point no more than fifty metres from the runway. We were so close to the field that we could see the green glow of the instruments in the cockpit. In between take-offs and landings, we would see three or four pinpoints of light disappearing into the distance and then circling back. We had come at a good time, as there was clearly a flight training program in progress. The noise was deafening, but we were absolutely transfixed by this experience. After watching our fifteenth take-off, we reluctantly returned to the base to get a good night's sleep in readiness for our early start.

The plan was to rise early, pack our gear, assemble in the dining room for breakfast and then move to the departure building where we would board the Hercules C-130 for our flight to Honiara. The morning was crisp and clear. A magnificent sunrise silhouetted the huge craft on the tarmac in front of us. By the time we had been checked off the passenger manifest, had our passports sighted, and had received the brief instruction on safety procedures, the sun had risen and the sky was a crisp blue. I hadn't been on a Hercules since the missions to East Timor and I was excited at the prospect of another trip on one. I had talked up the experience to Mel. I wished that Caro had been able to experience a Hercules flight during our first two missions to the Solomon Islands, but on those occasions, we were only offered commercial flights.

Mel couldn't wait to board the aircraft. Subtly, every Hercules is different. I had told her about the rather spartan forward seating arrangement, but to my surprise, the fuselage contained a different seating system altogether. In all other respects, the Hercules was as I remembered it, but this time, in addition to the bright orange-red webbing seats that lined the sides of the fuselage, there were also parallel seats down the middle of the aircraft. Our equipment and luggage was loaded into the rear of the aircraft. Before long, the engines roared to life and we were away. As we more or less had the plane to ourselves, we were free to move around the cabin and look out of the windows once the aircraft had left the tarmac. We spent the next three hours chatting to our fellow team members and reading before the aircraft touched down at Henderson International Airport. I looked out and could see that there were still a few large camouflaged army tents at the airport, but the military presence had largely been scaled down since our last mission. Predictably, the weather was hot and humid, although it was overcast.

As we had arrived in a military aircraft, the group disembarked as one and headed towards the airport lounge. There was no need to produce our passports and go through customs and immigration. Many members of the Regional Assistance Mission to Solomon Islands (RAMSI) force were there to meet us. One member, Detective Acting Inspector Darryl Huppatz stepped forward to introduce himself. After the formal introductions, he threw me a set of car keys, taking me entirely by surprise. To our great joy, Mel and I had been assigned a 4WD vehicle for our own personal use for the duration of the mission. We greatly welcomed the prospect of being able to move independently from our hotel to the mortuary and to the RAMSI base for our early morning departures to the Weathercoast without relying on RAMSI personnel. It was a white Toyota Hilux tray-truck. It was plastered with mud and reeked of wet carpet, as is the norm in the Solomon Islands. Someone had inscribed the name 'Ellen' in the dust and mud on the passenger side door, so we christened the car Ellen. Mick had been assigned his own vehicle and the remainder of the team hopped onto a minibus. We then headed off to Guadalcanal Beach Resort (GBR) for a pre-mission briefing session.

The outline of the mission was presented using a site map to show the locations of the planned exhumations. We discussed timelines for the transfer of the team to the sites, the return trips to Honiara, post-mortem scheduling and equipment needs. Although we all knew we might not be able to complete all the autopsies in the time we had, the mood was optimistic. Despite the doubts of some members of the team, Mel and I felt confident that we would be able to complete the twenty-two autopsies with the right balance of time in the field and time back in the mortuary. In addition to the exhumations and post-mortems discussed at the meeting, a further case awaited my attention. I had been warned about this case before our departure, but given the circumstances of the case as I understood them at the time, I didn't think it would interfere with the workflow of the mission.

We were to exhume the bodies from the villages of Ravu, Pite, Inakona, Ghaliatu, Bonegi and Malagheti. We were told that about half of the bodies were in single or double graves and the rest were in mass graves. We learned that the Ravu site contained eight bodies and the Pite site had at least one grave containing three bodies and an adjoining grave containing two more. I quickly realised that the site at Ravu could well be a relatively small grave with eight bodies unceremoniously dumped one upon the other, referred to as 'commingling' by forensic pathologists. With advanced decomposition, there was the potential here for a forensic nightmare. The worst-case scenario would be a pit of bones, which would be an anthropological jigsaw. I thought the best course of action would be for Mel and I to be present at the mass exhumation at Ravu and

Pite. The team agreed that my forensic input would be invaluable at these two sites. Through past experience, particularly in East Timor, I knew that the exhumation of a single body, or even two bodies in a grave, was not a logistical problem for an experienced team. To make the best use of our time, I was happy not to be directly involved in the exhumations at the remaining sites.

After the meeting, Mel and I were allocated a large backpack each, which we would keep for the duration of the mission. They each contained a mosquito dome tent, groundsheet, inflatable pillow, cooking utensils and other sundries necessary for an overnight stay in the jungle. After collecting several cartons of bottled water, Mel and I made our trip back to our fondly remembered Kitano Mendana hotel at Honiara. As usual, the staff recognised us instantly and welcomed us as old friends. Since our last stay in January, the hotel seemed to have had a facelift. Slowly but surely, the Mendana was lifting its game. The rooms were a little more tidy and the beds had bright new bedcovers. There had also been some improvements to the pool and bar areas. It had been a long day and we had a five thirty start in the morning, so we had an early night.

First thing the next morning, we set off for GBR. At that time of the morning, the roads were clear and we made it in twenty minutes. After a quick breakfast in the dining room, we were to meet with the team to take a shuttle bus to Air Point of Departure (APOD) where the helicopters would be waiting for us to take off at seven thirty. Mel and I are both chopper junkies, our favourite 'big toys', and we couldn't wait for our next fix. We arrived at APOD where two Hevi Lift helicopters waited under a canopy. The air was crisp and clear, perfect for the twenty-five minute flight to Ravu village on the Weathercoast. Before long we were airborne and although we had a grim task ahead of us, we were able to enjoy the panorama of the dense jungles and steep ravines that opened up beneath us.

RAVU

The villagers of Ravu had no doubt seen helicopters overhead from time to time, but we were told that this was the first time that a chopper had actually landed at the village. The excited locals arrived on the beach as we landed. The blast from the rotor wash was enormous and sand was flying in all directions. We got out and unloaded our gear onto the beach. As the first chopper lifted off, a second one approached and landed. It was not possible for all of the team to fit into one craft, so a helicopter shuttle service had been put into place. Intuitively, we either turned our faces to the jungle or crouched away from the chopper to avoid the fierce blast of sand from the rotor wash. We implored the villagers to do the same, but they could not take their eyes away from the helicopter landing before them. They would have been picking sand out of their hair and eyes for days.

Ravu beach is idyllic and belies the savagery that had occurred there many months before. The broad expanse of beach ceases abruptly, with the palm trees giving way to jungle. We walked less than a minute to the village to drop off our gear, as the villagers had graciously allowed us to stay there. The village was a simple affair. There were many grass huts and custom gardens were located close by. The villagers welcomed us, but were not overly interactive. As I had encountered in many cases of exhumation in jungle villages, the locals kept their distance and watched us a little warily.

We had sketchy details of the happenings at Ravu village. Apparently members of the Guadalcanal Liberation Front (GLF) had based themselves at the village and this information was known to the Joint Operations Group (JOG). It was alleged that members of the JOG had attempted to arrive at Ravu by boat, but were ambushed by Harold Keke's men and slaughtered. This was a particularly politically sensitive mission and the RAMSI personnel were rather guarded about exact details. The victims were from Kwaio, an area of neighbouring Malaita. The only information we had was that the captured eight victims were allegedly assembled on the beachfront and made to face the ocean. From an elevated point at the interface of palm trees and sand, the group were reported to have been summarily executed by automatic gunfire. Harry referred to the victims as the 'Kwaio boys'. Mel and I thought he had meant choir boys, until he explained the details of the tragic event more fully.

After settling in, we made our way to the gravesite, which was located no more than ten minutes walk into the dense jungle behind the village. To my great surprise, we saw a large, open grassy field, about the size of half a dozen tennis courts, next to the gravesite. I thought that this would have been a good spot for the helicopter to land, but the rotor wash would have blown the roofs off the village huts nearby, thus compounding further any possible ill-feeling. The locals pointed out the gravesite; we were grateful that it was located under some large, shady trees. Mick and other members of the DVI team then pegged out a tape perimeter. After a sweep of the surrounding area with the metal detector, the digging began. Fortunately, the reddish-brown soil was loose and our efforts were not plagued by stones and rocks. It must have been hard work for the killers of the Ravu eight.

After many hours, a gravesite three metres square and one and a half metres deep was exposed. After a time, the first body was uncovered. The first victim had been reduced to almost a skeleton. Mummified remnants of soft tissue were adhering to the torso and limbs. I noted the telltale crumbly blue-green material against the chest of the victim. The presence of oxidised bullet jacketing immediately indicated that this man had been shot. Several hours later, all of the remaining seven bodies had been exposed. The problem of potential commingling was not as bad as I had feared. Although several of the bodies were lying on top of each other, most overlapped each other only slightly. Once we had established the orientation of the bodies, separating and removing them was a relatively straightforward task. As dictated by protocol, we laid down metal numbered markers as each body was unearthed and exposed, so that an accurate photographic record could be made.

We exhumed the majority of the bodies by the end of the first day. Several of the bodies were buried deeper and into the side of the grave than we had anticipated, so we decided to leave them there until the following morning and to resume the digging the following day. The area was secured and several of the team and I went to the beach to the site of the alleged killings to see if we could find any ejected cartridge cases. We gave it up after about an hour, as we couldn't find anything, and made our way back to the village to set up our tents and prepare our evening meal.

My prowess as a camper had advanced little since my time at Marasa; Mel's was non-existent. I strained to remember how to assemble the mosquito dome tent, but after half an hour of exasperation, I humbly asked for assistance from one of the RAMSI members. As I was shown how to assemble my tent, Mel watched intently and followed the instructions. Before long, our tents were assembled among the many others gathered within the small perimeter of the village at the beachfront.

Doxycycline is wonderful stuff. It is the anti-malarial drug of preference for the Solomon Islands and is taken by the majority of the RAMSI personnel. Aside from the dreaded Doxy moment, which had struck at Marasa, it does have other untoward side effects. Mel and I had begun taking it the day before our departure and, as this was now day three, we were experiencing the inevitable abdominal cramps and the Doxy dumps had set in before arriving at Ravu. We had brought some Imodium with us to prevent the potential embarrassment of an urgent Doxy dump while in the field. We figured it was better to 'brick up' than be caught out.

We prepared our evening meal, which consisted of the usual contents of the by now infamous rat-pack, on the small camp stoves under lantern light. There was the inevitable swapping and bargaining to avoid the 'spag bol' and Dutch hot-pot, which were not to everybody's taste. The mosquitoes were very active, and although we generously applied repellent to our arms, legs and faces, they were unrelenting. The Weathercoast is renowned as a haven for the anopheles mosquito.

After our meal, Mel and I went for a nature walk. Many narrow tracks lined the beach and penetrated into the deeper jungle. Before leaving for this trip, I had bought a particularly powerful dual headlight, which incorporated both quartz halogen and xenon lamps. The beam from the xenon lamp could illuminate trees up to fifty metres away. As we carefully trod the narrow jungle paths, my xenon beam picked up the glittering red jewels of reflected light from the eyes of the spiders hidden in the trees and bushes. The entomological night life was absolutely astounding and Mel joyfully pointed out many species of spiders to me. She was able to name them and tell me all about their unique habits and lifestyles. Large toads were everywhere. As the xenon beam strafed the jungle and small streams, myriads of bright orange red points of light reflected back at us. The toads ranged from large creatures twice the size of a human fist, to small babies. Once we saw a large toad sitting on a rock and six smaller toads arranged in a circle around it. We felt as though we had interrupted the toad while it was holding court. I bitterly regretted not taking my camera with me. We returned as the others were settling down for the night, so we retired into our small mosquito domes. It had been a long, hard day and sleep came easily.

Bright and early the next morning, we were woken by the familiar village sounds of roosters crowing and dogs barking. We also heard some rather unusual rustling sounds around the tent. One of the village women was sweeping the sand between the tents to remove any leaves that had accumulated during the night.

After a quick breakfast, we returned to the gravesite to exhume the remaining bodies. As well as the enormous amount of camping gear we had brought, the helicopters had also brought eight metal military coffins to transfer the bodies back to Honiara. We photographed the bodies, removed them from the pit and placed them in the coffins to be taken back to the beachfront. Then we all grabbed shovels and filled in the large pit, leaving the ground smooth. We thanked the villagers for their cooperation and waited for the chopper that would take us back to Honiara. Before long, we heard the whump, whump, whump of the rotor blades in the distance. Again, the villagers rushed to the site to watch the bird land on the beach and were covered in sand from the rotor wash. A helicopter transfer service had been organised for the pickup from Ravu beach back to the small landing strip in the jungle next to Mbambanakira village.

The plan was to unload the helicopter at the Mbambanakira landing strip, assemble as a group and await the landing of one of the two remaining DHC-4 Caribous. The Caribou is a fascinating aircraft; it needs only a very short airstrip for take-off and landing. Once it has gained power, it takes off like a sling-shot. The Caribou was a valuable workhorse for the RAMSI personnel during earlier missions.

The Caribou lumbered along the landing field, turned about and dropped its tailgate. The coffins and equipment were loaded into the belly of the craft. We got on board and saw that the seating arrangement was similar to the C-130 Hercules, with all the passengers sitting in webbing seats lining the interior of the fuselage. At the instant of lift-off, the G forces were considerable and we all had to hang on tightly to the webbing to avoid being tossed towards the back of the aircraft in spite of the seatbelts we wore. The smell coming from the coffins was overpowering, even though the bodies were largely skeletonised, so when we reached cruising altitude, the loadie dropped the tailgate for better ventilation through the cabin. Neither Mel nor I had been on a Caribou before, and we were both enthralled by the experience.

The following day we were to begin the autopsies of the Ravu victims. Now that Mel and I were independently mobile, we agreed to meet the three RAMSI members and one member of the RSIP at eight o'clock the following morning to begin work. When we arrived at the gates of the mortuary behind the hospital, we saw that very little had changed since January. Happily, the management of medical refuse had become more sophisticated. Dedicated 44-gallon drums and sharps containers were regularly in use, replacing the random and exceedingly dangerous practice of disposing of such material onto the grass out the back of the hospital. The drab colours of the small mortuary were uninviting and somewhat oppressive. In addition, we noticed that the level of cleanliness had declined somewhat.

## LITTLE BONES

It was time to attend to the case that was awaiting examination that was not related to the twenty-two exhumations. The scenario was a

tragic one. I was told that a seven-month-old child had been allegedly struck to the back of the left side of the head by either the
handle or the flat side of a machete. Immediately after the blow, the
child had lost consciousness and had then apparently fitted and
become flaccid on one side of its body. The incident had occurred
in a village on one of the islands off Guadalcanal. The infant had
ultimately died and had been buried at Talise village. The father
had been arrested and the investigating team awaited my report.

A small, degraded wooden coffin was laid out on the post-
mortem table. I removed the tiny lid to reveal the fully skeletonised
remains of the infant, entwined with myriads of plant roots. The
little bones were completely devoid of flesh. I removed the bones
from the coffin with great care, and was able to reassemble the
skeleton. Many of the tiny bones of the hands and the feet had
dissolved during the process of decomposition. The infant's skull at
this age has not yet fused. All components of the cranium were
dissociated, but were easily reassembled. The occipital plate of the
cranium (the back of the skull) revealed a small, linear fracture
measuring nine millimetres in length. This was the only forensic
finding, but it seemed to substantiate the notion that the child had
been struck. I was to return in July 2005 to give evidence in this
case. Several alternative scenarios were put to me by the defence
during the trial, but the finding of the fracture in that location and
the acute neurological deterioration seemed to validate the story.
The accused was ultimately found guilty and sentenced to life
imprisonment.

Mel and I turned our attention next to the first two bodies
exhumed from Ravu village. Both were extensively decomposed
and largely skeletonised, so the examination was relatively straightforward. After cleaning the bones, we were able to say with great
confidence that both of these individuals suffered the effects of

multiple gunshot injury. We retrieved fragments of bullet jacketing from both bodies and found a spent cartridge case in the soil surrounding one of the bodies. This pattern of injury was to be repeated many times over in the remainder of the victims. The autopsies were concluded by about four o'clock, so after writing up my notes and cleaning out the mortuary, we headed back to the Mendana for a shower, a swim and a bite to eat. We were due to start again early the following morning, so we turned in early.

PITE

The following morning, we were up at five thirty and drove Ellen to GBR. After a quick breakfast and transfer to APOD, we flew out on a Caribou to Mbambanakira and from there, by helicopter to Pite. Pite (pronounced pee-tay) is now infamous in that many bodies I had examined previously had been buried there, including several of the Melanesian missionary brothers. Mel and I had christened the area 'The Pit of Pite'.

The beach at Pite is typical of the beautiful beach areas along the Weathercoast. We were scheduled to commence exhumations that morning and spend the night on the beach in our mosquito domes and depart the following day. The campsite was set up on the beach next to a small walking track leading to the village. Again, the villagers massed on the beach to watch the helicopters land and inevitably copped a severe sandblasting. Once the gear was unloaded, we transported all the materials to the nearby gravesite. We were told that there was one gravesite containing three bodies and a further site nearby containing two further bodies. The DVI team had brought a portable marquis that would act as a sunshade for the large exhumation site.

There was some doubt where the site containing the three

bodies was. The local villagers were circumspect and gestured vaguely towards the undergrowth. Their suspicion of us was palpable. We felt that they knew exactly where the site was but were reluctant to tell us directly. One villager said that they were not too sure where the bodies were buried, but that we should be careful of the water pipe. This comment was intriguing. Clearly, they knew the spot, because when digging began there was a likelihood that we would strike a water pipe leading from a tank high in the hills to the village.

We pulled aside the undergrowth with rakes revealing fine, black sand. Digging was easy in this environment. Before long, the spades scraped along a white PVC water pipe, indicating that we must be in the right area. Sure enough, just slightly inland from this and deeper down, we could smell decomposing bodies. The sand meant that occasionally the edges of the gravesite would cave in, so we used large plywood boards to act as retaining walls. About one and a half metres down, the spades uncovered a thick layer of rotting coconut palm fronds. This layer had been placed over the bodies. As the first body was revealed, we realised that we would have to extend the pit further inland to reveal the remaining two victims.

The smell of decomposition was overwhelming. At home, I inevitably have to deal with decomposing bodies, but generally not this decomposed. The bodies were so fragile that even gentle manipulation and movement of the limbs caused the body parts to dissociate. We removed the first body without incident and placed it on a blue body bag next to the grave's edge. The second and third bodies were overlapping and the advanced state of decomposition meant that we could not easily work out the exact anatomical relationships. Mick became concerned as the daylight faded, and suggested that we cover the bodies and resume at first light. I had been studying the bodies in the gravesite for some time and thought that if we rolled one body aside, then we could easily extricate the second body from underneath. I finally persuaded Mick to my way of thinking, and within half an hour, we had retrieved both bodies safely. A cursory examination of one of the bodies at the gravesite revealed an extensively shattered cranium, which immediately suggested to me a high velocity gunshot.

As the first exhumation was taking place, a second team was exploring an area nearby where it was thought the further two bodies were buried. This team had no luck. In spite of moving the dimensions of the grid to the right and left, forward and back, they couldn't find the bodies. We had the following morning to continue the search before the helicopter was due to pick us up.

The time had come to pitch out tents again on the beach-front. Mel and I had slowly gained some skills in erecting the small igloo-type mosquito domes. In no time at all, thirteen tents were erected adjacent to the pathway to the village. The large marquis tent had been moved to the beach so that we could set up our camp stoves for the evening meal. It was good to relax after a difficult day and enjoy the evening sea breeze. Mel and I again took a night walk away from the track towards the village. We crossed several small streams and encountered many amazing examples of insect life, including the ubiquitous toads. In spite of the tranquillity of the beachfront, I had a fitful sleep due to the intense humidity, which seemed to be magnified in the enclosed space of the mosquito dome. I lay sweating profusely for what seemed like an age before I eventually dropped off.

Early the next morning, after breakfast, we returned to the gravesite. We extended the boundaries of the second area, but still couldn't find the other two bodies. By the end of the morning, tonnes of fine, black sand had been shifted from one place to the next. We had either been given inaccurate information, or the landscape had changed in the interim. The information seemed to hinge on the position of a small coconut sapling, but looking around, there were many small coconut plants that had sprung up recently. As time was running out and the helicopter was due shortly, we decided that there was no point in digging any more. We shifted our digging equipment, tents, sundries and the metal coffins containing the three exhumed bodies to the beachfront for the first helicopter approach. We made a bonfire on the beach and threw in clothing and any combustible refuse to destroy any chance of contamination. Although the villagers would probably have appreciated the clothing, we didn't want them wearing anything that was tainted by decomposed bodies. The choppers came and transferred us to the airfield at Mbambanakira where the Caribou was waiting.

The following day, I performed the post-mortem examination on the three bodies exhumed from the first Pite gravesite. All bodies were grossly decomposed and extremely fragile. There was a surprising amount of fleshy tissue attached to the bones and I put this down largely to the protective layering of coconut fronds, which had been placed above them. The grave had also been deep and moist, which had preserved much of the soft tissue of the victims. Two of the victims had died from gunshot injury to the head, while the third had suffered catastrophic blunt force trauma to the chest, resulting in multiple rib fractures. In addition, two of the three bodies had incurred significant blunt force trauma to the face. The midline fracture to the mandible seems almost to be a signature injury in the Solomon Islands. The previous missions had disclosed very similar injuries. It appeared that these unfortunate victims had been tortured before the death blow or gunshot. They were almost certainly kicked in the face, or hit with gun butts.

Over the following two days, we examined the remaining six of the Ravu eight. Predictably, these victims all showed the telltale skeletal trauma of multiple gunshot injury. I identified oxidised bullet jacketing in many of the corpses. I also found several small degraded lead projectile cores and removed them from the bones. One of the victims had suffered from extensive and repeated trauma to the chest as well as multiple areas of gunshot. Another of the bodies had a catastrophic gunshot injury to the leg. We were told during the course of the exhumations that at least one of these individuals had been shot while in the boat as it had advanced towards the beach. Perhaps it was this man who had been struck by a GLF bullet.

Once the Ravu eight had been examined, I was able to examine the trajectory of most of the bullets that had been fired. They had been randomly showered over the victims, hitting the head, torso and limbs. The paths of many of the bullets could be accurately traced by examining where they had entered the body and where they had come to rest internally. The angles of the projectiles strongly suggested that the assailants had fired their weapons from an elevated position. The findings were in complete accord with the events that had been described to us.

## INAKONA AND GHALIATU

On 12 and 13 May, the exhumation team had visited Inakona and Ghaliatu on the Weathercoast, and had exhumed a further six bodies for our attention. These exhumations had proceeded without incident. The bodies were either in shallow, single graves or, at worst, two bodies in one grave. The exhumations had been uncomplicated and virtually entire skeletons had been delivered to us at the mortuary. On 14 and 15 May, Mel and I examined the six bodies from these two locations. They were easy examinations, although this time the bones were relatively clean. This saved us about an hour in reconstructing the skeletons and completing the examination of each victim. In what was by now a depressingly familiar scenario, the injuries ranged from extensive blunt force trauma to multiple gunshot injury. Again, the characteristic fracture to the mandible was identifiable in many of the victims.

An interesting twist took place during the examination of the Ghaliatu cases. A woman working at the hospital had asked whether we had examined the remains of her son. She thought her son may have been one of the bodies that we had failed to recover at Pite. She gave the RAMSI officers very precise information as to the location of her son's grave and also said that if she was taken to the spot she would be able to show us where the graves that we had missed were. The DVI commander decided to return the team for one working day. There would be no overnight stay and we would recover what we could in that time. I could sense pessimism about what we would find. At best, we may recover the two we had missed the first time; it would be a bonus if we could find the woman's son and the other young man who had been slain with him.

Early the following morning, the team assembled at APOD for the Caribou transfer to Mbambanakira and, from there, after unloading our gear, helicopter transfer to the village at Pite. The woman had been flown to Pite the day before to verify the location of the gravesite. I had immense respect for her courage. Not only was this her first time in a helicopter, but she had the courage to return to her son's grave, point it out and also indicate where two others lay. It could not have been easy for her. As it turned out, we had missed the second site by only one metre. The two bodies lay slightly further inland beyond our original perimeter. The two skeletons lying side by side were photographed and carefully placed into body bags.

The woman's son and his companion were at a separate gravesite some metres to the west of this site. She said that we would know her son, as he was carrying a colourful, woven bilum bag. Sadly, that is exactly what we found on one of the two bodies. These two bodies were removed after being photographed and placed into the waiting body bags. This brought the total body count to twenty-five, including the remains of the small baby.

On 18 May, Mel and I examined the remaining bodies from Pite, the two that had been missed and the two additional bodies located by the woman who worked at the hospital. Again, there was a tragic array of extensive blunt force trauma and gunshot injury. The woman approached me at the mortuary after we had finished for the day. She asked me whether her son had suffered before he had died. One of the victims had been shot in the head, clearly a merciful end. The woman's son, in contrast, had incurred multiple areas of blunt force trauma to the chest. It was difficult to say with any degree of certainty whether her son had died quickly or not. In spite of this, I assured her that he had. Tears welled up in her eyes as she thanked us profusely for taking the time and the care to exhume and examine her son's remains and she was hopeful that his bones could be returned to the family very soon. We had to explain the process of confirming identity by DNA. Thankfully, she understood why it would be some time before the family could reclaim the body for burial. The lady gave Mel and me a tearful hug, thanked us again and went back to her duties at the hospital. We never saw her again.

## BONEGI BEACH

During the days of the examination of the bodies from Inakona, Ghaliatu and Pite, the team had been busy at Bonegi Beach just west of Honiara and Malagheti. These were the last of the planned exhumations; once these bodies had been examined, our mission would be complete.

The recovery of the bodies at Bonegi Beach had been easy. The team had had no trouble finding the gravesites, which were thankfully rather shallow. Both bodies were completely skeletonised, which of course made our jobs much easier. It was just a matter of brushing the sand off the bones and in some cases washing them, before laying them out and examining them. Each post-mortem was concluded in around an hour.

One of the bodies from Bonegi proved to be problematic. Several small fractures were identified on the ribs, but not significant enough to cause death. There was a suggestion of drowning, however. In the intact body, there are no diagnostic findings in drowning, and certainly not in skeletal remains. I labelled the cause of death as unascertained, with a significant comment raising the issues of the circumstances of death and our negative findings. The second body was much easier. The victim had suffered extreme blunt force trauma to the head. There was no doubt about the cause of death in this case. It would have been due to beatings with a heavy, blunt object, probably a gun butt.

The last body exhumed was from a village at Malagheti on the Weathercoast. The body had been exhumed on 15 May and it was to be our last case at the mortuary. The circumstances of this man's death were outlined to me. It was alleged that he had been punched and kicked multiple times and made to walk a distance before he ultimately collapsed and died. During his last journey, he repeatedly complained of thirst. My clinical background told me that this man had died of shock and almost certainly internal bleeding. Would I be able to find sufficient trauma to the skeleton to explain his protracted death? The skeleton was perhaps the cleanest we had received to date. Within minutes, we had the bones laid out ready for examination. The man had indeed suffered episodes of repeated beating. The shoulder blades were fractured, as were several of the spines of his lower back. This was consistent with his being kicked, punched and possibly being struck with gun butts. The only significant findings were fractures of the ninth and tenth left ribs. Anatomically, these ribs overlie the spleen. From my experience of other cases on the island, I knew that many of the locals had enlarged spleens due to the effects of endemic malaria. An enlarged spleen is a fragile spleen, which can readily rupture given sufficient force. Intuitively, I knew that this man had died of internal blood loss secondary to a ruptured spleen and, although I only had bones to look at, it seemed an entirely reasonable cause of death given the circumstances.

After eight full working days in the mortuary, the last six being consecutive and without a break, we had finally completed our mission. We had performed twenty-five autopsies, two more than originally planned, and we had undertaken an additional impromptu mission to Pite on the information provided to us by the woman at the hospital. Despite the doubts expressed at the meeting at GBR before our departure to the Weathercoast, we had come through with flying colours. The team as a whole were delighted with the results of our work.

Mel and I had had little time during this rotation for any rest and relaxation. We had the occasional free afternoon to travel around town and to visit old and familiar places. We had also enjoyed several nights out at the local restaurants in Honiara, interspersed with meals in our hotel rooms. We were due to fly out early in the morning on 21 May, which left us one clear day to take Ellen out for a road trip. Having this rugged 4WD vehicle, we took the road west of Honiara, stopping briefly at Bonegi Beach. Beyond Bonegi, the road becomes a mere goat track and peters out at the extreme west of the island. We passed through several small but swift-moving creeks and eventually found a pretty, secluded beach where we had lunch and a bit of a paddle. Turning the car around, we returned to Honiara and the road east through the broad expanse of plantations until a ruined bridge caused us to stop, turn around and head back home. In that day, we had traversed the entire north coast of Guadalcanal. Mel preferred the eastern plantation end, while my preference lay with the dense jungle and fast-moving streams to the west.

We spent the following morning lounging by the pool and doing some last minute souvenir shopping for the folks back at home. We had organised a late checkout from the Mendana and headed back to GBR to return Ellen to the car pool. Our flight was scheduled for two o'clock the following morning, so for the rest of that afternoon and evening, we sat under the sundeck at GBR, read for a bit and chatted with the RAMSI officers. Several hours before we were due to head back to the airport for our departure, the most intense monsoon rains I have ever seen hit the resort. The rain was coming in at a forty-five degree angle. We were lucky to have got away with the exhumations on the Weathercoast without being subjected to these often forceful seasonal deluges, for which the Weathercoast is renowned, sometimes exceeding five metres of rainfall annually. I had been lucky at Marasa and Sughu and we had got away with it yet again at Pite and Ravu.

In spite of the rain, the level of humidity at the airport terminus was insufferable. Leaving at two in the morning is not pretty. There is always the chance for a quick nap in transit, but we seemed to arrive at Brisbane shortly after our departure and had to pass through customs and immigration one more time before the last leg of our journey home to Melbourne. We finally arrived home around nine in the morning, hailed a taxi and headed home.

It was nice to be home, but also sad to leave the Solomon Islands. Mel in particular had developed a strong affinity with the Islands and longed to return. I would return in November to give expert evidence in a murder trial, and before long would find myself back there as part of my planned activities for sabbatical leave. While we had been abroad, Mel and I had discussed possible projects for an extended humanitarian mission into the Solomon Islands in January and February 2005.

# TEN

# SABBATICAL

Sabbatical leave is a privilege offered to specialist medical practitioners and academics during the seventh year of tenure. It is not a time for annual leave, but an opportunity for them to pursue further study in their specialist field, attend conferences, publish or engage in research. As a young doctor and a junior registrar, it seemed that the boss or a senior consultant was always away on sabbatical. When I joined the Victorian Institute of Forensic Medicine (VIFM), I knew that my sabbatical leave would come around eventually, but it always seemed years and years away. And now my sabbatical was due to begin on 1 January 2005. For several months, I had been thinking about what I would do during my six months away from the Institute. I naturally thought of forensic work in the Solomon Islands.

In October 2004, I made a proposal to the Australian Federal Police (AFP). Up until then, all the work I'd performed in the Solomon Islands had been on a contractual basis. Now I could offer my time to the AFP without government expense. This proposal was accepted wholeheartedly and I was to leave Melbourne on 20 January to spend five weeks in Honiara to perform further exhumations and post-mortems and carry out some other humanitarian projects I had in mind.

Towards the end of the year, things came unstuck. When Adam Dunning, a twenty-six year old AFP protective service officer in the Solomon Islands, was shot and killed in late December, priorities within the AFP changed. As well as this, there was a general shift away from exhumations and post-mortems in favour of police induction and training programs. As my proposal had been accepted, and in the interim I had declined other offers, I suggested that I should go all the same and at least complete some of the humanitarian work that I had in mind. Steve Olinder, with whom I had worked closely in East Timor, was now based in Honiara. He had set aside three exhumed bodies for my attention, but no further exhumations were planned in the near future. Based on my previous experiences, I fully expected that fresh cases would come to light during the five weeks of my rotation.

On Boxing Day 2004, my plans for the first few weeks of the new year changed radically.

## ASIAN TSUNAMI

I watched the tragedy of the huge tsunami unfolding on the news bulletins on television along with the rest of the world and was horrified by the mounting death toll. I thought that the VIFM would almost certainly assist in the identification process of the many thousands killed in the affected areas. I rang the Institute and left a message with Associate Professor David Ranson, offering my services. I was well placed to go at short notice as I was not due to leave for the Solomon Islands until late January. This would allow me to give three weeks to any help that the Institute organised.

As the death toll mounted, I received a call at home on 27 December. Dr Michael Burke, one of my colleagues from the VIFM, was the homicide pathologist on call at that time. He had just received a phone call from Dr Peter Ellis, the Director of Forensic Pathology at Westmead Hospital in New South Wales. The small circle of practising forensic pathologists in Australia has contingency plans for mass disasters. It is the responsibility of the directors of the forensic institutes to identify staff who are available to leave immediately to participate in any mass identification exercise. Michael had been contacted but was not able to go to Thailand at that time and was asking me whether I would be able to go instead. I said I could and he told me to contact Mick Travers, coordinator of the Disaster Victim Identification (DVI) team.

I was surprised when I was able to contact him immediately on his mobile phone, as I fully expected that he would be receiving a barrage of calls. I was told to catch the next flight to Thailand and that there would be a quick stopover in Canberra en route. I expected that I would depart early the next morning, but to my great surprise, I was told the flight would be leaving Tullamarine airport in two and a half hours. I barely had enough time to pack the essential items into a single suitcase, call a taxi and go.

In the departure lounge at Tullamarine, I met up with several police officers from the Victorian Forensic Science Centre who would act as fingerprint experts and scene photographers. The flight left on schedule and we landed at Canberra airport, where Mick Travers and other staff from the AFP met us. After a short briefing session, the contingent then boarded a chartered flight to Phuket. The Australian contingent to Thailand consisted of two pathologists (Peter Ellis and me), photographers, fingerprint experts, forensic odontologists and coordinators. We were the first to arrive in Thailand. The usual holiday atmosphere of this popular tourist destination had vanished. We drove through the hushed and empty streets to the Phuket Hilton where we were to stay. We were all issued a room each in the huge, but now deserted hotel. We spent the rest of the day sorting through the multitude of large storage cases containing post-mortem equipment, specimen containers, fingerprint equipment, photographic gear and other essential items.

Many of the dead had been taken to Wat Yan Yeow, a Buddhist temple at Khao Lak. The following day, we drove along the coast road in a convoy of 4WD vehicles to Khao Lak, approximately 150 kilometres north of Phuket. The trip took about three hours. We finally arrived at the ornate gates of the large temple complex at Wat Yan Yeow, which is bounded by a rectangular perimeter adjacent to a river. The long distance between our hotel and the temple created a logistical nightmare in the days and weeks ahead. We spent six hours a day travelling to and from the site where the dead bodies lay.

The cars finally came to a halt in a side street and we unpacked our gear and headed into the temple. We all knew that we were about to encounter a horrifying scene, but none of us was prepared for what we saw. There were more than nine hundred bodies on the ground. In every direction, bodies were laid out in orderly rows and, in some areas, there was barely sufficient room to walk between them. Virtually all the bodies were in the early bloat phase of decomposition. Many lay uncovered, while others had been concealed with body bags and groundsheets. Tragically, there were many young people, children and babies among the dead. As we wandered around the sea of human devastation and tragedy, we could barely comprehend its extent. We were openly moved by what we saw and many of us rang home at this time to speak to our work colleagues and loved ones. None of us had ever encountered anything like this before. We were completely overwhelmed by the enormity of the task before us.

The challenges were enormous. There were no mortuary facilities and no refrigerated containers to halt the decomposition process. This would make identification increasingly difficult. Fortunately, these vital facilities would materialise over the next four days. Peter Ellis and I rapidly designed the floor plans to transform a large, open prayer house into a temporary morgue. Within a few days, a false ceiling had been installed, plywood walls had been put up and full lighting, air-conditioning, running water and sinks with drain holes seemed to appear from nowhere. The original plan was for three working post-mortem tables, but this number was later extended to five as the demand for body examination increased.

The time spent waiting for the mortuary facility to be prepared was not wasted. I worked in the field on the preliminary examination of the bodies. This involved unzipping body bags and giving the details of the gender, clothing, jewellery and visible distinguishing marks and scars to the police officer who was acting as a scribe. It was essential to complete this process extremely thoroughly and efficiently. Many of these bodies would not see the light of day again for several weeks. Further decomposition would be retarded once the refrigerated containers arrived, but in the meantime, subtle clues to identification would be lost as the bodies lay out under the scorching sun.

I had the dubious honour of performing the first autopsy four days later in front of approximately sixty people. As we refined the process, and as the autopsy facility and refrigerated containers became available, we were able to very quickly construct an effective assembly line of body identification. The first step was to retrieve a body from the refrigerated container. Next, the body was taken to the fingerprint section. During the early days, the bodies were relatively well preserved. The skin of the fingers is quite thick and resilient and for some time it remains durable and amenable to fingerprint examination. Then the body would be sent to the mortuary for us to examine.

Peter and I and the other international forensic pathologists then performed our function. The body was photographed and washed down for the first time. The post-mortem phase was run according to DVI protocol, and along the lines that I had already begun with the bodies as they lay waiting outside. We measured the height of the body with a ruler, noting any distinguishing marks or features that would assist with the identification process. We were specifically looking for tattoos and scars from past surgical procedures. We examined, washed, photographed and set aside personal items such as jewellery, watches and clothing. The autopsy process was different from what I was used to because this was a scene of a mass disaster, not a crime scene, and the cause of death was never in question. The autopsy was fairly brief, consisting simply of a quick internal inspection of the abdominal cavity to ascertain the presence of the gall bladder, appendix, uterus and other incidental pathology that may be encountered. Many of the bodies had not undergone any severe degree of trauma and it was presumed that these unfortunate individuals had drowned as the wave had rushed through the coastline, annihilating whole villages. Some victims had lethal crush injuries to the head, chest and limbs.

The body was then handed over to the odontologists, who meticulously charted the dental record. They took specialised dental x-rays and charted all the dental landmarks on a pro-forma. In time, dentists from around the world would forward dental records for comparison and, hopefully, identification. After taking samples for DNA, the body was then returned to the refrigerator and would not be released until absolute confirmation of identity weeks or even months later.

As the number of international pathologists grew day by day, the temple was barely large enough to contain them. Many local people had volunteered to help transport bodies from the refrigerator to the mortuary and also to prevent the spread of disease as many of the bodies lay in the hot Thai sun. The Thais had the enormous advantage of being able to discriminate between national and international victims. A body identified as a Thai national would have a piece of red string attached to the wrist. A body identified as an international would have a piece of yellow string attached. This was the entire basis of identification that was given to us initially. Bodies brought in later in the process could not be identified by either Thai specialists or us due to the advanced degree of decomposition after days spent lying in the hot sun.

As we struggled to process the nine hundred bodies and to come to terms with the tragedy, we were shocked when a further six hundred bodies arrived. Over the next few days, the body count would rise to in excess of two thousand. Over six thousand people had died along the coastline of Thailand as the wave hit the beach area. Many were international travellers and holiday-makers. The number of confirmed Australian dead made up only a small proportion of the total.

After about a week of commuting daily from Khao Lak to Phuket (three hours each way) and spending up to eight hours in the field, the international teams came on board and we were able to roster different teams on so that examinations could be performed twenty-four hours a day. Towards the end of my rotation, the number of refrigerated containers had increased to thirty-two, all containing between forty and fifty bodies. As the international teams joined in, we examined approximately four hundred bodies in five days. We were very heartened by these phenomenal results, given that we had come to the scene with absolutely no facilities.

Towards the end of my rotation, a second temporary mortuary facility was nearing completion. A second, large, open prayer house, which had previously contained many hundreds of bodies, had now been cleaned and refurbished very much like the first mortuary we had commissioned two and a half weeks earlier. This new facility would contain a further ten workstations, and would be manned on a twenty-four hour work roster.

The first contingent was due to return to Australia in mid-January. Peter and I said our goodbyes to the team on 12 January. I have since found out that the last of the Australian victims have been formally identified. The work, however, is ongoing. Many of our forensic odontologists have made several return visits to Thailand to help in the protracted and taxing process of identification of further international and local victims.

## RETURN TO THE SOLOMON ISLANDS

The tragic event of the Asian tsunami had not altered my plans to return to the Solomon Islands, which Mel and I had been planning for some time. It did mean, though, that I hadn't been back to work after the Christmas break and now had a rather short week to sort out loose ends before leaving on 20 January. As well as examining the three exhumed bodies that Steve Olinder had placed in cold storage, we had planned in advance several specific projects. We had made arrangements to spend the five weeks in Honiara in a small, rented house where we would be basically self-sufficient. But the AFP had generously granted full accommodation for us for the duration of our stay and so we headed back to the tried and true Kitano Mendana Hotel. Very little had changed since my last visit.

The staff, as usual, were extremely welcoming and recognised us immediately from previous missions. It was as if we had never left. On this occasion, we were even assigned adjoining rooms on the ground floor.

## MAGNUM OPUS

Whenever I was in the Solomon Islands, there was always a possibility that a subpoena might be served on me without notice. To this end, I brought my large binder containing all of the post-mortem reports that I had compiled since the very first mission in September 2003. As a specialist forensic pathologist seconded to the Regional Assistance Mission to Solomon Islands (RAMSI), I had performed all of the militia-based autopsies from September 2003 to the present day. I had also examined other contemporary homicides and suspicious cases not directly related to the militia killings. Mel and I realised that the next five weeks would be an ideal time to produce a definitive report on the forensic activities during the time of RAMSI. The enormous binder, which weighed several kilograms, was an invaluable resource.

We began examining the contents of the binder the following day. The post-mortem reports were very complete and we also had access to the circumstances reports, which were partly available to me at the time of autopsy and also archived at the Prosecution Support Unit at Honiara. Using this material, we were able to pull together all the relevant information. We identified the geographic areas where the killings occurred and made sense of the scenarios and the factions involved. We worked at this project passionately on and off throughout the following five weeks. We believe that this is a definitive work and may act as a valuable template for other forensic missions in the future in the Solomon Islands and elsewhere, particularly Papua New Guinea.

The report is over a hundred and forty pages and many photographs are yet to be included. It covers the evolution of the politics in the Solomon Islands from the Second World War, how the rival factions evolved, where the major events occurred and the relevant scenarios in an accurate chronological timeline. It also includes a summary of the autopsy reports with a detailed analysis of the wound patterns and valuable material such as an instrument inventory and the post-mortem protocols we used. We incorporated recommendations, pitfalls and difficulties and how we overcame them in the field and in the mortuary. Lastly, we included a detailed appendix outlining the distribution of gunshot wounds, skeletal injuries and items of clothing received at the time of autopsy. All good reference works require an accurate glossary. To this end, Mel, with her formidable computer skills, was able to isolate all relevant medical terms and between us we translated these terms into common usage for the lay reader. We were acutely aware that this report would be read not only by forensic specialists, and police investigators, but also by prosecution, defence and other interested parties. We sincerely hope that at some time in the future the AFP will endorse this document.

## MORTUARY RENOVATIONS

As part of my detailed proposal to the AFP, I had volunteered my time to completely renovate the small, basic mortuary facility at the National Referral Hospital at Honiara. This proposal was accepted wholeheartedly. Before we left Australia, we had submitted a list of sundries such as paint, paintbrushes, rollers, solvents, silicon fillers and dropsheets. The AFP and RAMSI provided the hardware and we were to provide the elbow grease. We spread out the large dropsheets and got ready to begin the first phase of our renovation project.

Inevitably the water failed on the first day. Mel called out, 'Hey buddy, the water's on the fritz!' (The exact context and extended conversation stays on the island.) The only source of water nearby was a lonely upright pipe next to the hospital incinerator near the beachfront. Undaunted, we set up a bucket brigade to bring water to the mortuary so we could at least begin cleaning all the surfaces that were to be repainted. We brought up enough water to begin and spent the next five days cleaning the floor, benches and shelves and scraping away loose paint. It was a labour of love and Mel in particular was incredibly enthusiastic. As she began sanding the painted surfaces, I armed myself with a caulking gun and filled many of the gaps between the white-tiled walls behind the sink and work benches and also along the tiled half-wall of the mortuary room.

The room itself is about the size of a single car garage with many recessed areas, such as shelving at multiple levels, and nooks and crannies where plumbing is attached to the sink. Having completed the surface preparation, we began painting. The original colour scheme was ghastly. The walls were a dirty off-white, tan colour. The edges of the bench and shelving were a bilious green. The ceiling had dulled over time and didn't reflect the light from the fluorescent strips overhead very well. The large area of ceiling that had been installed during our mission in October 2003 was still bare masonite. It took many coats of paint to obscure the original colours, but, after five days, the improvement was dramatic. The room seemed to be one and a half times its original size because of the improved reflection from the internal lighting. The guys from RAMSI could not believe their eyes. It was now a mortuary to be proud of, and, having completed this massive task, we were ready to examine the first of the bodies that Steve had set aside for us.

Part of the humanitarian component of my sabbatical leave in the Solomon Islands was to assist in the education of the local surgeons who are occasionally required to perform medico-legal autopsies. Over the following weeks, I was twice able to demonstrate correct forensic post-mortem technique on fresh bodies. To help further, the VIFM generously donated two textbooks on forensic pathology.

CASEWORK

On 7 February, we examined the first case in our newly renovated post-mortem facility. This time around, we felt as though we were working in a facility that could be found in the basement of a teaching hospital, rather than a ramshackle shed. We followed the usual procedure of photographing the victim, describing the clothing, separating the clothing and any other evidentiary items and ultimately cleaning the bones and laying them out for final inspection. We were able to conclude each case promptly, including the writing up phase at the conclusion of each autopsy.

The first victim we examined was a grossly decomposed elderly male, one of two militia killings that were case-related. He had died a violent death as a result of blunt force trauma to his torso. Many right and left ribs were fractured. We were informed before the autopsy that it was likely that the man had been shot, but I could find no evidence of this. The man's t-shirt was riddled with holes, but they seemed to have been caused by degeneration of the fabric through wear and tear, rather than gunshots.

We performed the second case four days later. Mel and I were present, along with Serena Buxton as photographer and Steve Hunt as evidence officer. Also present were three observers who were familiar with the case. Although it now looked much larger, the small room barely accommodated seven people and the temperature and humidity rose to extremely uncomfortable levels. This victim was an elderly female, the wife of the victim we had examined four days earlier. She had suffered severe blunt force injuries, including extensive rib fractures on both sides, facial fractures and a single high-velocity gunshot wound to the chest. This case in particular stands out from all the rest in my mind. The vast majority of cases that I had examined since 2003 consisted of young men of military age. This was the first female fatality I had examined and the fact that it was an elderly female made the circumstances of this case seem more tragic. It brought home the ferocity of members of some militia factions. I wondered how such horrendous injuries inflicted on a helpless elderly female could seem justified in anybody's mind.

## INCIDENTAL CASES

As was so often the case when I was in the Solomon Islands, some 'While you are here, Doc' cases materialised. These incidental cases were usually suspicious cases requiring investigation that were not related to the militia. As I am the only forensic pathologist to visit the islands, I seem to be a magnet for such cases.

Early on the morning of 12 February, we had received a call from the forensic investigation team to attend a potential crime scene. As we had organised a hire care for our stay, it was easy for us to attend a scene at any time and any place. This gave us the flexibility to travel to and from the mortuary, as well as anywhere else we may need to go, including meals at local restaurants.

We were called to a Second World War watchtower located close to Henderson Field. The body of a well-nourished male had been found lying face down in the tall grass at the base of the tower. It was not clear whether the man had jumped, been pushed, or merely slipped and fallen from the tower. After inspecting the tower and potential jump or drop points, Serena suggested that it might have been from a height of ten or eighteen metres, but we could not establish this with any degree of certainty. Clearly this man had been on the ground for some time. Fly eggs had been deposited around his eyes, hair, nose and mouth. It was an enormous advantage that Mel could attend this case. Using her forensic entomological expertise, she was able to work out that the man must have died some time the previous day, as flies do not lay eggs after dark. In addition, the man's body had already begun to decompose. There was prominent marbling of his skin and marked gaseous distension of the abdomen. The autopsy examination disclosed the expected trauma after a fall from a height. I found extensive internal blood loss secondary to rupture of both liver and spleen. I didn't find any offensive or defensive type injuries, however. How the body came to be at the base of the tower remains a mystery; the investigation of this case is ongoing.

Two days later, there was a further case. This man had died after an altercation outside one of the local food outlets. The injuries found during the external examination were minimal. Aside from a small laceration to the lower lip, there was little else to indicate that he had been involved in a fight. But the internal examination revealed that the man had suffered an extensive traumatic basal subarachnoid haemorrhage. In common language, this man had suffered severe bleeding around his brain after having one of the major arteries severed as a result of significant external trauma. This is the type of case that often causes enormous angst back home. The vertebral artery is a well-concealed vessel that runs through the spines of the neck before it enters into the base of the skull. Any forceful trauma to the side or the back of the head, particularly involving sudden flexion, extension or rotation, may potentially tear this vessel. At the VIFM, this type of case would require detailed radiological assessment and even excision of the cervical spine to meticulously examine and identify the point of vessel rupture. But the reality was that we were in the Solomon Islands and couldn't perform that level of investigation. The trauma was clearly apparent and there was obvious bruising to the side of the head once the scalp was reflected, so the exact point of impact was an academic issue.

The third incidental case materialised a week later and re-minded me of the trauma that I was accustomed to in East Timor. This man had died as a result of an alleged machete attack. The story that investigators had been told was that the man had fallen onto a knife. They were not convinced by this explanation and the analysis of the injuries did not support it either. As there was great interest in this particular case, a further five observers joined us for this examination.

We began the examination in the crowded, hot and humid room. There was a large, incised wound on one of the victim's legs, which had severed a medium calibre artery. Elevating the limb and applying a tourniquet would almost certainly have prevented his death, but this had not been done and the man had bled to death slowly in the back of a utility on the way to the hospital. That it could have been so easily prevented made this death all the more tragic. Suspicious cuts to the hands indicated that the man had attempted to defend himself against an assailant wielding a sharp blade. These defensive injuries spoke strongly against accidental injury by falling upon a knife. Inevitably, this case will come before the courts.

We performed our last case two days later. This was the last of the three exhumed militia-related cases coordinated by Steve Olinder. This victim had been bound at the wrists with nylon rope and had been savagely beaten and then shot. The litany of injuries read like many of the reports I had compiled previously. I found extensive rib fractures on both sides, the inevitable fracture to the jaw, and, in this case, a through-and-through gunshot injury to the upper back. Although the bullet passed through the man's body, the telltale skeletal trauma said it all. I wrote up the final report and all our cases were done.

After we concluded this case, Mel and I set aside a half day to do one last thorough mortuary clean up. We wanted to leave the mortuary in the best possible condition, particularly as we had spent so many hours bringing it up to its present magnificent state. Once we had finished and closed the mortuary doors for the last time on this mission, we drove back to the hotel with an enormous sense of pride. We had accomplished all we had set out to do, and more.

In addition to the mortuary makeover, examining the three militia killings, the incidental cases and the writing of the report, we were also pleased to be able to attend the first days of Harold Keke's trial for the killing of Father Augustine Geve. Father Geve was a Catholic priest who was backed by Keke supporters when he ran for the South Guadalcanal seat during the 2001 elections. When he became Minister of Youth, Women and Sports in Kemakeza's government, Keke and his followers turned on him. Keke publicly admitted on a live radio broadcast that he had shot Father Geve for misuse of public funds and dishonesty.

Mel and I had seen many pictures of Harold Keke in his heyday. Most pictures show him with a closely cropped beard and short haircut, either with a maniacal smile or a menacing scowl, and toting a heavy calibre semi-automatic weapon. We sat in the observers' gallery and watched as Keke was marched into the courtroom by Australian protective services officers. During his incarceration, Keke had lost a considerable amount of weight. He had also lost his beard and opted now for a rather unruly set of dreadlocks. We did not hear him utter any words during our time in the observer's gallery, but on many occasions, he would lean forward, rock to and fro, roll his eyes towards the ceiling and giggle to himself. We could only imagine what was going through his mind during this trial.

We left for home on 24 February. We were to learn several weeks later that Harold Keke, together with Ronnie Cawa and Frances Lela were convicted of murder in the first degree for the premeditated killing of Father Augustine Geve and would spend the rest of their lives in Rove prison.

This was to be the first of many trials concerning the notorious Guadalcanal Liberation Front (GLF) leader and his henchmen. During the months of May, July and August 2005, I returned to the Solomon Islands to give expert forensic evidence in the case of six of the seven slain Missionary Brothers and two contemporary homicides. Even now, there is a strong undercurrent of support for Harold Keke in Guadalcanal. The fact that the prosecutions unit is going to proceed with all cases involving Keke and his men speaks loudly and very clearly to the population that this man is a despot and will not be released any time soon. It is extremely satisfying to know that the work I have done is contributing in some measure to gaining justice for the dead.

It seems ironic that the majority of the court cases I have attended in the Solomon Islands relate to the contemporary non-militia killings rather than the ones that have hit the headlines in recent times. These cases are of course no less significant in the eyes of the grieving families—justice must be served at all levels. The process of committal and trial for alleged militia killings is expected to continue and will be a long and ongoing process. I have been informed that I can expect to return to the Solomon Islands on perhaps another four occasions during 2006 for this purpose. A further round of exhumations and autopsies is also being organised and coordinated. During my last visit to Honiara, a proposal was put to me to return yet again to undertake perhaps ten to fifteen additional cases.

# EPILOGUE

It is inevitable, and also tragic, that our inhumanity to one another will ensure that the forensic pathologist of the present and future will be kept busy. In very recent times, we have all witnessed the tragic aftermath of terrorist attacks and bombings. The forensic pathologist is integral to the investigation and successful prosecution of these abhorrent events. I have not been part of the investigation of such an event, but I will. Sophisticated radiological imaging like the CT scan and MRI will never replace the skills of the experienced forensic pathologist. The law courts will always demand the expert testimony of the pathology in cases of suspicious deaths, mass disasters and obvious homicides.

I was proud to have been part of the first Australian contingent to Phuket. Although the most ghastly scenario I have been a part of, this mission taught me an enormous amount about the intricacies of disaster victim identification, a skill which sadly will be required again. I feel privileged to have been the first forensic pathologist in East Timor after the referendum killings, to have had the opportunity to work as a specialist on rotation to Kosova and to be the first and only forensic pathologist to perform examinations in the Solomon Islands group.

To say that I am a war junkie is not that far from the truth. I find that the challenges placed upon me in third world countries and in adverse conditions can bring about surprising and very satisfying results. I think it brings out the best in me at a professional and personal level, and it does the same for the other professionals I have had the pleasure of working with. Without exception, all personnel who have volunteered their time in East Timor, Kosova and the Solomon Islands have been people of the highest calibre. The passion and dedication displayed by my co-workers, particularly in Thailand, is unsurpassed in my professional experience.

I have been blessed in my career and have no regrets about my change in direction from general practice to forensic pathology. I would wholeheartedly recommend young medical graduates and undifferentiated registrars to seriously consider this sub-specialty as a career option. Forensic pathology can be as routine or exciting and demanding as you want it to be. In spite of what television, the media and cinema suggest, the forensic pathologist does not work in isolation, but is merely one small cog in a large machine, heavily reliant on the input from the specialists who are integral to the investigation of the case or disaster. *Quincy M.E.* has a lot to answer for, but I am grateful for its influence when I was a young, impressionable youth in my late high school years. I've never looked back.

# Timeline

- **February 2000: East Timor**
  First forensic pathologist to conduct formal post-mortem examinations in the post referendum period. Fifty-one autopsies performed in two weeks—most of which were related to the Passabe massacre.

- **May 2000: Kosova**
  Forensic pathologist on rotation with the British Forensic Team examining victims of ethnic cleansing. Sixty-four autopsies performed in three weeks.

- **October 2000: East Timor**
  Two non militia related autopsies performed—one homicide and one suspicious death.

- **February 2001: East Timor**
  Eleven autopsies performed including exhumations at Ainaro, Aituto and Cassa.

- **July 2002: East Timor**
  Twelve autopsies performed including exhumations in Dili and Liquica.

- **December 2002: East Timor**
  Autopsies performed on two gunshot fatalities and examination of fifteen survivors of the mass shooting in Dili. Also conducted an autopsy on one suspicious death.

- **September 2003: Solomon Islands**
  First forensic pathologist (and only to date) to be involved in exhumations and post mortem examinations of atrocities allegedly committed by the warlord Harold Keke. Three cases exhumed—all autopsies performed at grave site in jungle environment.

- **October 2003: Solomon Islands**
  Performed the autopsies on seven bodies (Melanesian Missionary Brothers) and one contemporary homicide in Honiara.

- **January 2004: Solomon Islands**
  Examined the victims of ten militia killings and three contemporary homicides.

- **May 2004: Solomon Islands**
  Performed twenty-five autopsies and fifteen exhumations.

- **November 2004: Solomon Islands**
  Appeared as an expert witness in the High Court, Honiara.

- **December 2004: Khao Lak, Thailand**
  Member of the Disaster Victim Identification Team which was part of the first Australian contingent to Thailand after the Boxing Day tsunami.

- **January 2005: Solomon Islands**
  Performed an additional six autopsies. Renovated the mortuary and compiled a definitive report of all forensic activity occurring in the Solomon Islands during the RAMSI intervention.

- **May 2005: Solomon Islands**
  Gave expert forensic evidence in the High Court, Honiara. Performed a further two autopsies.

- **July 2005: Solomon Islands**
  Further expert forensic evidence in the High Court, Honiara.

- **August 2005: Solomon Islands**
  Further expert forensic evidence in the High Court, Honiara.

- **October 2005: Solomon Islands**
  Further expert forensic evidence in the High Court, Honiara.

- **January 2006: Solomon Islands**
  A further twelve exhumations and autopsies to be conducted. Trial concerning death of Brother Nathaniel Sado to commence.

# Recommended Reading

**East Timor**

Breen, Bob. *Mission Accomplished: East Timor*. Sydney: Allen & Unwin, 2000.

Dunn, James. *Timor: A People Betrayed*. QLD: Jacaranda Press, 1983.

Dunn, James. *East Timor: A Rough Passage to Independence*. 3rd ed. NSW: Longueville Books, 2003.

Martinkus, John. *A Dirty Little War*. NSW: Random House, 2001.


**Kosova**

Judah, Tim. *Kosovo: War and Revenge*. USA: Yale University Press, 2000.

Malcolm, Noel. *Kosovo: A Short History*. UK: Yale University Press, 2000.


**Solomon Islands**

Fraenkel, Jon. *The Manipulation of Custom: From Uprising to Intervention in the Solomon Islands*. New Zealand: Victoria University Press, 2004.

Griffith, Samuel B. *The Battle for Guadalcanal*. USA: University of Illinois Press, 2000.

Miller, John. *Guadalcanal: The First Offensive*. USA: Konecky & Konecky, 1948.

Mueller, Joseph N. *Guadalcanal 1942*. UK: Osprey Publishing, 1999.

# Index